WOUNDED

A little souvenir
of your stay here
with us. (We loved having you!)

God Bless you,

love

Catherine Engels

Also by Bob and Barbara Hitching

THE
WOUNDED

Bob and Barbara Hitching

OM Publishing

PO Box 48, Bromley, Kent, England
PO Box 28, Waynesboro, Georgia, USA

British Library Cataloguing in Publication Data

Hitching, Bob
    The wounded.
    I. Title   II. Hitching, Barbara
    823'.914 [F]

    ISBN 1 85078 067 6

OM Publishing is an imprint of Send The Light
(Operation Mobilisation),
PO Box 48, Bromley, Kent, England, BR1 3JH

Production and Printing in England by
Nuprint Ltd, Station Road, Harpenden, Herts, AL5 4SE

We would like to dedicate this book to dear friends in London who have been wounded.

Acknowledgements

We would like to thank Shirley Connelly, Linda McAndrew, and Dorothy Holloway for their help in typing the original manuscript. Kit Huff and Kathy Young proof read and corrected the first manuscripts. Then when our computer broke, erasing much work, Tom Young came to our rescue, finding much of the lost material, and Steve Bailey repaired the computer. During major preparation of the final manuscript, Linda and Greg Morton took our children for four days, providing us with a quiet atmosphere to work, so we could meet our deadline.

We are also grateful to Dave Brown, our publisher, who has been a friend to us. Ruth March, our editor, patiently went over each manuscript. We also wish to thank each of our friends who encouraged us and who prayed for us as we worked on this book.

1

When it rains in the East End of London, it seems as if a grey mist descends from some distant twilight zone, covering the area with drabness, like a blanket. Nick Thompson was used to the weather and, in fact, seemed to be comforted by its familiarity. Brushing back the damp sandy brown hair that curled over his forehead, he walked down Commercial Road, through the market by Whitechapel Underground Station. In spite of the rain, there was a bustle of activity, as Indian, Turkish, and English merchants shouted the value of their wares. The market was a spot of colour in the drab greyness of the area, and the increased volume of noise seemed to indicate that its presence provided an aura of excitement in the monotony of life.

Nick turned into the station, purchased his ticket, then ran over the stairs to wait for a train to go to Liverpool Street. There he would catch the 149 bus, up to Dalston Junction, and then walk through the back streets of Ridley Market, up to where Stoke Newington and Stamford Hill met. Today was Saturday, and Nick felt that certain kind of Saturday morning feeling. How he loved the East End, he thought. People milled about him, the air filled with various noises as trains pulled in and out of the station. Pakistani women, holding shopping bags filled with every conceivable produce, sought to comfort little ones, who in varying stages of tiredness were either crying or laughing, while several Sikhs wandered up and down the platform.

In the midst of all his ruminatings on Saturday mornings, and the East End feeling, the train he was waiting for slowly squealed to a stop. Nick made his way into the carriage, passing three young fellows, who were sitting, staring blankly into space. Their heads were almost bald, but for the barest traces of stubble. One of them wore a leather jacket with the words, 'Death to the Pigs' and 'Anarchy Rules' written in bold white letters. Another wore a denim jacket with 'Death to the Yids' written across its back. Nick walked by them with the sense of uneasiness one feels in such a situation. In the far corner, a neatly dressed young man wearing a yamaka was reading the Jerusalem Post. It seemed inevitable that some sort of action would occur, what with three teenagers who looked like something from a horror movie, sitting in the same carriage with a young Jew. For a moment, Nick calculated the potential chemical reaction, but before he could do anything, the automatic doors quickly shut.

Almost at the same moment, the three rose to their feet and started walking towards the Jewish fellow. The train swayed from side to side, making their movements look strange, causing them to appear even more hideous than they were.

Standing just a few feet away from the young man, the leather-jacketed walking billboard for anarchy and death spoke. 'Here Yid, we don't like you on this train.' He sneered, 'Fact is, if you don't get off at this next stop, I'm gonna crack your head open.'

The reaction from the Jewish youth, as he sat quietly and continued to read, was so profound that it pierced Nick's soul. He was not ignoring his tormentor; rather he was shutting his soul off into an inner sanctuary that was unreachable by the outside world. It was almost as if he was placing a notice on the outside of his being, saying to the world around, 'Out to lunch'.

Without any further talk, one of the thugs snatched the newspaper from the youth and threw it to the ground. He growled at his potential prey, 'Didn't you hear him, you slimy little Yid? We don't wanna be on the same train as you. Got it?'

Knocking the young man's yamaka to the ground, he reached out and grabbed him by the throat. Suddenly Nick Thompson, the carefree fellow, happy just to be alive, lost control. 'Why, you mindless moron!' he shouted making his way towards the group. 'You filthy scum...' As his right foot struck out, the denim-jacketed thug fell to the ground in pain. The fellow in the leather jacket lunged towards him, but Nick quickly flashed two fingers into his attacker's eyes, who screamed with pain. The third decided no action was the best action. Seconds later, the train pulled into the station, and the three dragged themselves from the train.

The young Jewish fellow stood in utter amazement at the sight he had just seen. 'My word! Where did you learn to fight like that?' Trembling, he leaned over, picked up his crumpled newspaper and dusting off his yamaka, placed it back on his head.

As the train had approached the station, someone had pulled the emergency chain. Now a guard came pushing through the crowd gathered around Nick and the Jewish boy. Nick, visibly shaken, opened his mouth to speak, instead, smashed his fist into his other hand, and groaning, collapsed onto the seat, resting his elbows on his knees, and holding his head in his hands. The next few minutes were chaotic as everyone was milling around, trying to find out what had happened. A young Pakistani with a cockney accent was excitedly relating how this man with his head in his hands was really a hero, and that he had never seen such an incredible fight before.

Eventually the guard was able to move the people away, and the train was allowed to continue on its way.

Kenny sat silently next to his new-found friend. Somehow they were bonded into a friendship based on tragedy. The Jewish lad reached out his hand to Nick. 'I'm Kenny Levinson...' Looking down at his crumpled newspaper and then directly into Nick's eyes, 'Thanks for what you did. They would have pulped me.'

Nick nodded and spoke softly, 'It's O.K. Sorry that they gave you all that "Yid" stuff. I don't know how you can stand it day in, day out...'

Kenny shrugged his shoulders, 'It's not a point of standing it, it's always been that way, and always will be...but,' he hesitated, 'look, don't get me wrong. You saved me...but I don't understand. Why are you so upset? I mean, here you are this tasty geezer who comes ploughing into three blokes; you knacker one, almost turn the other into a blind man...then you sit down acting as if the world had ended.'

Nick, his eyes narrowed, pressed his lips together, then looked out of the window as the train pulled into Liverpool Street. 'I've got to get off here.' He stood up to leave.

Kenny also rose. 'So do I. Where are you going?'

'Up to Stamford Hill—how about you?'

Kenny smiled, 'Me too. That's where I live.'

Together they got off the train, and made their way to the bus stop. The rain that had shrouded the city in grey, had given way to a hazy, half-hearted attempt of the sun to make its way past the clouds.

'Listen, I don't want to get inside your head, but tell me, why is it that you look so uptight?'

'Well,' Nick hesitated, 'it's like this. I've been around a bit...you know, agro, kickings and stuff. Well, a couple of weeks ago, I gave my life to God.'

Kenny looked confused. 'I don't get it. What does that have to do...?' Then it all came together in his

12

mind. 'Oh, I get it. You're a Christian!' He mockingly laughed. 'Can you imagine? You're a Christian and you saved a Jew! I suppose that is just about the worst thing in the world that could happen to you. But why did you help me? After all, you Christians are supposed to hate Jews, not help them!'

'Wait a minute. What are you talking about? I'm sick in my guts because I did those geezers in, and I know Jesus wouldn't have done it that way. I've let him down and I feel sick. See, it was that look on your face when they first came up to you. It was like you didn't learn that look, you inherited it.'

Kenny was shocked. 'I'm sorry. I got it all wrong...but I don't understand. See, you've got to real-ise the word "Jesus" to me is a symbol for pain, unkind-ness, and humiliation. You know, Hitler was Christian and all that stuff.'

Now it was Nick's turn to look shocked. 'What do you mean, Hitler was a Christian? He was a monster!'

The 149 bus came around the corner at that moment, giving them a slight reprieve in a conversation that seemed to become more complex as each second passed. They paid their fares, and taking a seat, sat silently as the bus moved up Liverpool Street to the City Road round-about. As Nick looked out of the window, he noticed for the first time that all the shops had Jewish names...Goldstein, Reuben, Katz. The day's events had suddenly changed his perspective.

As the bus sat in the traffic before Dalston Junction, Nick spoke. 'Why don't we walk? Then we can talk some more about all this stuff.' Kenny nodded and both young men jumped off the bus as it stood idly in the traffic. 'Here, this is Saturday. Aren't you supposed to be in your synagogue?'

Kenny smiled and shrugged his shoulders. 'I made my appearance, but you know how it is. Religion, well, it's good some of the time, but...well, you know.'

Nick looked confused. 'I thought being Jewish was a nationality. Is it a religion or a nationality, or what?'

Kenny laughed. 'If we could work that one out, we would go down in history with Einstein and Napoleon!'

'But, if it's no big deal...you know, your religion...why wear that head gear and go around reading Jewish newspapers? Then you wouldn't have to put up with the nonsense we just went through.'

'Actually, I only wear my head gear, as you call it, when I go to see my grandmother. She always hassles me if I don't have it on. As for the newspaper, well, being Jewish is who I am. And who is to say I can't read what I choose to read?'

When the two parted some time later, and Nick promised to give Kenny a call, Kenny just smiled.

2

Early the following Friday evening Nick picked up the telephone to call Kenny. His mind had become almost obsessed with thoughts about Jews and Christians, and the conflicts that had been the basis for their historical relationship. 'Hey, Kenny. Yeah, this is Nick. Nick, you know, the Christian geezer that got into your agro last week.'

Kenny responded warmly, yet with a certain hesitation in his voice. Nick continued. 'Listen man, I was wondering if we could get together to do some more talking. Maybe you could come over to my place for coffee?'

Kenny sounded even more hesitant but agreed. 'Be around in about an hour then, all right? Cheers.'

Nick hung up the phone, walked over to the window, and looked out into the street. It was slowly becoming dark and the forms of the children playing in the street were becoming more like silhouettes etched into a shadow puppet stage. His pensive mood was suddenly broken as his sister walked into the room. Chrissy was wearing jeans and a red silk blouse. She had long, flowing, jet black hair. Nobody knew why, and so she had put up with the usual jokes about her Mum and the milkman from her earliest years. Chrissy's face was delicately sculpted. Huge brown eyes shaded by heavy black lashes were complemented by a creamy complexion. At nineteen, her figure nearly perfect, she was considered to be a beautiful young woman. To Nick, she was simply Chrissy. They had always been close, even though Nick was four years older than she. About three years ago, it seemed half his life was spent getting into fights to protect her from some bloke.

When she was eighteen, she had moved in with a second-hand car dealer in Walthamstow and the whole sordid affair had lasted less than six months. Returning home, she had wept in Nick's arms. 'It is a curse to be beautiful. No one wants me for who I am, all they are interested in is my body. Nick, I think I want to be a nun. Straight up. Just to get away from all of this.'

Yet now, as they stood together in the front room, things had changed. Nick was no longer Mr Kneecap Buster but was Holy Joe. Chrissy had changed too, becoming cynical about men, and generally avoiding them.

Chrissy spoke. 'What's happening tonight, Nick? Are you going out?'

'No, why?' he replied.

'Well, I was thinking about getting a video in and I was wondering if we could go halves on it. I want to get "The Blob Returns From the Grave".'

Nick laughed. 'You want to what?'

Chrissy looked surprised, ' "The Blob", you know, the geezer with three faces who lives in a swamp.'

'Chrissy, you want me to go halves on getting "The Blob"?'

'Oh, come on! Don't tell me that being religious means you can't watch movies like that?'

'I'm not saying nothing! Anyway, I got this mate of mine coming over for coffee.'

'Oh no! You're not bringing some weird religious fanatic here? It used to be that your mates wanted to get fresh with me, now I suppose all they will want to do is to save my soul.'

'This bloke's not a Christian. He's a Jew.'

Chrissy looked shocked. 'Does Dad know he's coming? He's always saying the Jews say "This is your flag, but our country." Fact is, I think some of Dad's mates on the buses are National Front members.'

Nick shrugged his shoulders. 'Well, he's coming over anyway. We were just going to talk a while.'

'Hmph.' Chrissy made a face and left the room, indignant that her brother's new-found religion now excluded him from going halves on getting videos.

Nick turned to the window again, the silhouettes now completely absorbed into the darkness of the street.

3

'Hey, come in man!' Nick greeted Kenny who was standing on the doorstep.

'Thanks. I haven't been around this area for years.' He looked about him as he walked into Nick's front room.

Nick nodded smiling, 'Actually, this used to be a Jewish area. In fact, I think your lot still own most of it, even though you all moved out to Golders Green, and then to Barnet.'

Kenny rolled his eyes, 'Not my lot! We're strictly the Stamford Hill mob. Never will we leave, till the Messiah comes, and all that.'

Nick beckoned Kenny to take a seat, then sat down himself. 'Actually, I was going to ask you about that. You know, up at Stamford Hill, you have those blokes with the black hats and beards, with the hair hanging down the side. Are you the same as them?'

'Well, it's a bit complicated to explain, but yeah, we're kind of the same. You see, we both believe that if you scratch a Goy deep enough, then underneath you will find an anti-semite. But those people are ultra-strict, while as reformed Jews, we're a little bit more liberal.'

As Kenny was speaking, Chrissy walked into the room, her raven black hair bouncing as she moved. Smiling at Kenny, she spoke, 'Hi. I'm Chrissy, Nick's sister. Excuse the gear I'm wearing. Actually, I'm a nun, you know, with Mother Teresa and all that, but we're trying to infiltrate London's youth culture. You know, make being a nun more desirable. I suppose Nick has told you he's really a monk...?'

Nick picked up a cushion and, laughing, threw it at Chrissy. 'Get out of here. This room is for intellectuals only, and your IQ is only about ten.'

Chrissy raising her eyebrows, did a quick 'Here's looking at you, kid,' Bogart impersonation, and left.

Kenny looked overwhelmed. 'Blimey, what on earth was all that?'

'That, my Jewish intellectual, was your introduction to an East End thermo-nuclear female personality. That is my prodigal sister, the very embodiment of energy and charisma.'

Kenny put on a mock Indian accent, 'I am telling you, do they be arranging marriages in your culture?'

Suddenly, without warning, the door flew open and Nick's dad stood in the doorway. Standing about five feet ten inches tall, and weighing about sixteen stone, he was wearing a rumpled T-shirt with braces that dangled down the sides of his trousers. The expression on his face was one of contorted rage. 'Nick! Get out here! I want to speak to you.'

Nick rose, looking helplessly at Kenny. Kenny had the same expression on his face as when he was on the underground. It was as if by instinct, he was able to close himself off to the outer world. There in the sanctuary of his private world, he would co-exist with the persecuted ghosts of Jewish history.

Nick and his father walked into their small kitchen. The kettle was just beginning to boil, and its whistle slowly began to eject an almost symbolic scream into the already tense atmosphere. Nick reached out and silenced its agony. His father spoke with anger and contempt in his voice, 'Have you completely lost your marbles, bringing a Yid round here? Pakis, I don't like. Wooftas, I hate. But a Yid is the worst of the bunch. You obviously don't know your history, son. About the Jewish Peril and all that...'

Nick crossed his arms and pursed his lips. As he looked at his father figure and model for life, spouting a lot of nonsense, he realised he felt ambivalence towards his dad. Before he had become a Christian, he had no conflict of feeling, as there was simply no love at all for the man. Now, he found his emotions to be like a battleground, combining a complex emotional morass of love, hate, pain, resentment, and anger that left him bewildered.

'...And do you know what they say about these little islands as they buy up all our land? They say, "This is your flag but..."'

' "But it's our country," ' Nick interjected. He had heard those words so many times he could repeat them backwards.

'All right! Just get the Yid out of here. And I mean, now!'

Nick turned and walked back towards the front room, the words 'Just get the Yid out' echoing in his ears, as if coming from a distance. Chrissy had been sitting on the settee next to Mum, watching the telly. Hearing her father, she stood up and followed Nick down the hall to the front room. Kenny was standing with his coat on waiting for them. No words were spoken as the three walked to the door and stepped out into the night. Kenny sighed as the latch snapped behind them; it was as if in his mind the gate of some concentration camp had just closed. Out here on the streets, there was freedom. Yet only limited, for the fact remained that he was a Jew. A bleeding Yid, a four-by-two, a Morrey. No matter where he went, he would be hunted down and punished just for being. Punished by words, or by fists and feet, or by the camps and gas chambers.

Nick called out as Kenny began to walk away, 'Listen, I'm really sorry man.' He groaned. Chrissy put her hand on his shoulder seeking to comfort him.

Kenny halted in his tracks, stood with his head bowed, then turned back. 'This is just too much for me to handle. I mean, what a wind-up, what a wind-up!' For moments, the three seemed locked together in an arena of pain that seemed to bind them together, a brother, a sister, and an adopted soul-mate.

A West Indian boy walked past them, and the rap lyrics blaring from his ghetto-blaster seemed to punctuate their agony. 'Welcome to a homeland that will never be yours' echoed through the street, as the young Rasta man walked away. Kenny shrugged his shoulders, grinned sheepishly, 'It's your flag but my country.'

4

The wooden door creaked open and three men in their early fifties walked into the smoke-filled private chamber at the rear of the Star and Garter pub, which was situated in a small back street off Bethnal Green Road. Harry Thompson, Nick's father, and Charlie Watson were sitting in the corner behind a round table. A dirty ashtray and two glasses of partially drunk light and bitter sat on the table. Those glasses were a symbol, a monument, a fraternal statement. Jim Whitehouse, Syd Stone, and Fred Davies entered the room and were soon settled at Harry's table. This group had known each other since they were children and had stuck together throughout the years.

Charlie Watson, short, balding, and overweight, had been around Valance Road when the Kray Brothers ruled East London. He had been one of Ronnie's young boys, part of a spy network in the East End underworld.

Harry Thompson worked as a bus driver on the 149 route, which took him through Stamford Hill, where the Jewishness of the community was more evident than in any other area of London. Hasidim, the orthodox group, lived here. The men wore beards. Both men and boys had long locks of hair which hung in front of their ears, were dressed in black, and kept their heads covered with black hats. Harry often spat out of his window as he drove through the area, as an act of contempt for the Jews.

Syd Stone worked in a factory in Wapping and lived in a flat in the same area. Fred Davies and Jim Whitehouse were unemployed. To Jim, the reason was crystal clear. 'The country's filled up with Blacks, Pakis, and Turks, let in by a Jewish conspiracy. It's those Rothschilds, using their money to take over the world.'

Although they were not card-carrying members of the National Front, they were sympathetic to the organisation, and even to the National Party, two of the most extreme groups in inner London's complex web of political parties. From time to time, each of these groups distributed literature, which the men read avidly and believed without question.

Harry greeted the newcomers, each of whom held a pint of light and bitter in his hand. As he turned to Jim Whitehouse, he asked, 'Jim, what was the name of that Yid thing? You know, the protocols of Zion stuff, about what the Yids are planning to do?'

Jim, the group's resident intellectual, who in their minds knew all that was possible to know on every subject under the sun, spoke with a cultivated middle-class accent when answering such questions. 'You mean the Protocols of the Learned Elders of Zion, the document that was secretly written by a group of rabbis about how they plan to take over the world?'

'That's it! That's it!' Harry responded excitedly.

Jim continued the symposium on 'Jewish history'. '*The Times* said it was a forgery, but they're controlled by the Yids. We know these protocols are their own writings, and that the Yids drink the blood of children that they sacrifice at Passover.'

Harry had all he needed to justify his outburst against his son's friend. 'I knew it! You know that son of mine actually had the nerve to bring a Yid into my house the other day. I had to kick him out, see. These kids! They

23

just have no idea what they're doing. I mean, a Yid in my house!'

Jim nodded seriously, 'Yes, it's this government that's the problem. The Jews have them completely controlled, same as the papers and the telly. They're all owned by the Jews. You know, they all meet in Zurich each year and plan how they will eventually take over the world.'

Sid jumped in, 'Same as the Yanks. Useless for anything.'

Jim continued. 'See, it's the Jews' propaganda that puts this stuff out about the Holocaust. There weren't no holocaust. It was the blooming Jews who killed the whites. Hitler came along and tried to stop it, then got clobbered by the Jewish controlled British lot and the Yanks.'

As this conversation continued amidst a haze of smoke and clink of glasses, another meeting was in progress in a small church hall in another part of the East End. Nick and four of his friends met every Tuesday evening for a Bible study.

Huss, short for Hussein, was a Turk from a Muslim background. His parents reacted strongly against him when he told them he had become a believer. When he was baptised, his father angrily accused him of becoming a Greek. Because of the deep hatred between Turks and Greeks, if a Turk became a Christian, and especially if he was baptised, his people believed that he had become a traitor to his nation. As such, his father, believing Huss had brought disgrace on the family, exploded with anger, declaring that he would never again be welcome in his home. Huss had shouted back and then later felt guilty for losing his temper.

Also in the group was an English married couple, Rick and Sheila. They had grown up together, and used to frequent the discos and clubs with Huss and Angie, his English girlfriend. Rick was twenty-three and worked as a clerk in the bank. He had blond hair, and wore glasses, which he was continually pushing back up his nose. He was tall and skinny, so much so that his friends laughingly said, if he turned sideways, all they would see was glasses sliding down a nose.

Sheila was a year younger, and in contrast, was a trifle on the plump side. Her short curly black hair framed a face with beautiful emerald green eyes, rosy cheeks, and full lips. She and Angie were very close, and one day Angie had confided that she wished to remain pure for the man she would marry. Some time later, she had begun to act strangely and had seemed to avoid the group. On a Friday evening, Sheila had received a call from a very hysterical Angie, saying she had just had an abortion and that Huss had dumped her. Sheila, furious with Huss for the callous way he had treated Angie, had exploded in anger when she got off the telephone, spitting on him and cursing him.

Then she had run through the house, collecting Huss's belongings, and thrown them out into the street. Huss, who had been living with them for a year, was devastated.

In his deep rejection, he had gone to see an old school friend, whose family had taken him in and provided a home for him. They were believers, who lived what they believed, and as a result, found joy in showering him with love. Thus, in spite of himself, Huss found himself being drawn to the rejected Jesus. Through this family, he began to understand that Christ had died in his place, taking the punishment that he deserved, so that he could find God's forgiveness. In the quietness of his room, late at night, he had prayed, asking God to become part of his life. The family had given Huss a New Testament, and he spent long hours studying it, writing down questions as he read. These he would take to his friend's father, and the two would sit up until the early hours of the morning discussing the Scriptures.

The following days revealed deep changes in his attitudes, along with deep struggles. Huss visited Rick and Sheila to apologise to them for his behaviour, and both had been deeply moved. Rick and Huss began to spend time together again, taking long walks, and talking over many issues. Rick had also been touched by the change in Sheila, who had become a believer. Finally, after long weeks of discussion, Rick realised that this man Jesus, who offered unconditional love, was the one he was searching for too. Within a week of becoming a believer, Rick agreed with Sheila that God would want them to be married rather than to continue to live together, outside the laws of both God and man. The following week, they were married at the registry office.

Angie had disappeared after seeing Sheila one last time; shortly after that, rumours began to circulate that she was a lesbian. When Huss became a believer a few months later, he had been overcome with guilt, knowing that he was responsible for messing her up. One day, walking through Clissold Park, he told God that as an act of penance, he would remain single for the rest of his life. When he shared that decision with the group, they had been impressed by his sacrifice.

Androulla, a Greek girl, was known simply as Roulla. Her long black hair, with an orange streak in the front, had been the point of endless discussions amongst the group. Should Christians, or believers, as they were more commonly called, dye their hair like that? No common consensus had been arrived at, but the conversation had certainly provided food for thought. Roulla's argument was that believers often were inconsistent in their judgements. For example, it was acceptable to have earrings but not a nose-ring. All seemed to agree that wasn't consistent.

Huss had black hair which was short on the front and long in the back, a bushy moustache, and dark skin. He had the strongest opinion in the group when it came to not winding people up because of what they wore, or what their hair was like. 'I think we need to be careful about condemning another person for external things. I knew a man who was very quick to condemn anyone who did not think as he did about outward things. He would get angry, sure the person was sinning. One day I happened to see him in W.H. Smith's at Victoria Station and started to go over to say hello. Then I realised he was reading a Playboy magazine. I learned from that not to focus on externals but to work on my heart and my attitudes, and eventually the outside would conform.' Huss turned to Roulla, 'Listen, Roulla, whatever the colour of your hair, we know your heart is clean and beautiful, and we love you.' That had then become the ideological cornerstone of the group.

It was this group of wounded, in the process of being healed, individuals who were the joy of Nick's life. Their honesty about everything was like a light shining into his own life. This Tuesday evening, however, he was discouraged because of the way his father had treated Kenny.

Roulla immediately sensed that something was bothering him. 'Nick, what's wrong, man? You look like you're carrying something heavy.'

Nick smiled and shrugged, 'You know that Jewish bloke I told you about last week?'

Rick responded, 'The one you saved by doing your Rambo act on those geezers in the train?'

'Right. Well, he came round the other day to my place. My old man gave me all this "Yid" stuff, then kicked him out.'

Roulla reached out and touched Nick's hand. 'That's horrible, Nick. You look really broken up about it.'

Nick looked down, then across the room. 'It was the look in Kenny's eyes after we went outside. They were like the eyes of a wounded animal; it was horrible to know I was partly responsible for his pain.'

Huss nodded his head, 'I know, man, what you're saying. It's like some people's problems are so deep because they can't protect themselves. Rick, Sheila and me know this bloke, from when we used to go down the boozer on Fridays. He was this Maltese bloke who had a wooden leg. Well, all the locals used to wind him up when he got drunk. When they called him the wooden Malteser, this little fellow used to unscrew his leg and take a swing at the geezers bothering him. But your Jewish friend can't fight, or protect himself.'

Nick broke in, 'See, that's the problem. If it was only the one bunch, then it would be easy. He could get some talent together and go and do a number on them. But...' He looked down at the floor, then around the table, 'but it seems like it's the whole world that is against him.'

Roulla spoke, 'It's true what you are saying, but what can we do to help him? Especially if he doesn't want our help. You know what it is like, people's pride often gets in the way, because who on earth wants to admit that they need anybody other than themselves?'

Nick looked at Roulla. Her sincere, gentle eyes seemed to contain a depth of concern that was immeasurable. As he looked at her, he realised for the first time that his feelings for her were becoming more than just that of friendship. As the conversation continued, he caught her eyes and smiled. She flashed back a smile, unaware of his emotions. Nick was brought back to reality by Huss saying, 'Listen, Nick, what you need to do is to bring him along here on Tuesday. Instead of us having a Bible study, we can have a discussion about Jews and Christians, and how we can love and care for each other.'

Everyone agreed that this was a great idea. Then Nick turned to Huss and spoke, 'Is there any news about Angie?'

'No,' Huss shook his head sadly, 'nothing new.'

'Why don't we pray about it?' Roulla suggested.

The group slipped to their knees, then spent some time praying for Angie, for Kenny, and for each other, that God would work in their lives.

5

The room had an empty, lifeless feel about it. A cassette recorder sat on the floor by the rumpled, unmade double bed in the far corner. There was a table with two chairs, two small cupboards, and on top of one cupboard was a Baby Belling cooker. The single light, with its naked bulb, hung about eighteen inches from the ceiling, whose paint was faded and peeling. Dog-eared magazines and various items of clothing lay scattered about the room. Dirty plates were stacked on the unwashed table, which was also cluttered with empty milk bottles and Chinese take-away containers. Above a rusty sink, hung a mirror, a crack making its jagged way from the top left-hand corner, down to the bottom right-hand corner.

Standing in front of the mirror was Angie. Her hair, which once had been thick and golden, was now severely cut in a butch crop. Her beautiful olive complexion had become yellowish, and oily in appearance. Her brown eyes, bloodshot with deep circles underneath them looked over-large in a face where the skin was drawn taut across the cheekbones. She was wearing a green oversize man's shirt, and a pair of baggy, combat green trousers. Now, standing before the mirror, she saw the reflection of a broken, defiled person whose life was empty and meaningless. The months seemed to slip away as her thoughts took her back to the bar in Bethnal

Green, just after her abortion.

Trying to drown her pain and the feeling of guilt, she had gone to the pub, where she had sat scrunched into a corner by herself, hoping no one would notice her. She had choked down a drink and then, feeling uneasy, had decided to leave. As she left, a young man got up and followed her.

Coming up behind her, he spoke, 'Hello, darling. I know how to make you happy.'

With a cry of fear, she had bolted, but he quickly caught her and, laughing, drew her to himself. Panicking, she began to scream hysterically. A middle-aged woman had appeared on the scene, swinging her umbrella and the man had run off into the night. Putting her arm around the sobbing girl, the woman, who said her name was Margaret, had taken Angie home to her flat.

Once there, Margaret lit a cigarette, and gave it to Angie. 'Here, this will help you.'

Angie inhaled, then coughed. 'What is this?'

Margaret smiled. 'Just smoke it, it will help you relax.'

Angie obeyed, and within minutes felt a warmth stealing over her.

'You look like you're going through a hard time. Has some man messed you about?'

Angie leaned back on the bed and, feeling totally relaxed, began to pour out her heart. 'I met this guy, Huss. He's a Turkish bloke. Well, he was handsome and seemed so nice. He always seemed to be interested in anything I had to say—you know? I fell in love with him. Everything seemed great. Then one day, the weather was so beautiful, and we decided to go for a ramble down Epping Forest. Well, we were walking along, it was all quiet kinda like we were in our own special little world. Then he pulled me to him and started to kiss me. It was like my dreams were all going to come true and he

31

would propose to me. Instead, he started to touch me. I tried to push him away. He, he wouldn't stop. I didn't know what to do. I kept crying and pleading, but he just laughed.' Angie faltered, the tears pouring down her cheeks. Taking a deep breath, she continued. 'When he wouldn't stop, I guess I just sort of detached myself from it all, and it was like I was outside myself, looking on at what was happening to someone else. After it was all over, and I was rearranging my clothes, he joked about me being a virgin.

'For six weeks I walked around feeling so dirty. It was like everyone that looked at me knew what had happened. I just wanted to hide, so I avoided everyone. Then, to my horror I realised that I was pregnant. I just didn't know what to do, so in desperation I went to Huss and told him. He mocked me and told me to go have an abortion. I felt so lost and scared; I found myself pleading with him to help me. He took me to the clinic, promising to marry me when we were a bit older. After the abortion was over, he laughed at me and told me he never wanted to see me again. Then he turned and walked away.

'Everything that was dear to me is lost. I dread the nights, a world of nightmares, where everything is beyond my control. I wish I could die. I feel so guilty and dirty, but I'm so scared.' Angie had bent over, holding her stomach, and rocking back and forth in pain as great sobs of anguish shook her body. Margaret had reached out and held her as she sobbed. Then, after making her a cup of tea, she encouraged her to rest.

In the following days, Margaret was very gentle as Angie was consumed with fear and grief. As she allowed her to weep and encouraged her to express anger at men, an emotional bond began to form, and Angie found herself responding to the concern the older woman showed. There seemed to be a never-ending supply of 'weed', and pills, which helped her to escape from the feeling of helplessness and unreasonable fear.

Then one night, high on drugs and alcohol, totally unaware of what was happening, the relationship progressed. In the morning, waking from a night of troublesome dreams, strange thoughts flitted across the screen of her mind, which she turned from in disgust. When Margaret returned to the room that evening, Angie learned that what she had thought were dreams, were indeed reality. In her weakness and need, she was caught in a web from which she did not know how to escape.

Now, as she stood looking into the mirror, memories overwhelmed her. The horror and betrayal of the rape, the desperate moment when she realised she was pregnant, running in fear to Huss, only to be told that she must have an abortion. The anguish as she lay on the table and the unprotected fragile life within was sacrificed to appease the pagan god of male pride. The horror of the abortion swept over her with nightmares of babies dying and being cut up, and the memory of Huss laughing at her and then leaving her weeping outside the clinic. The memory of the stranger touching her, then Margaret helping her, being so understanding and kind with her in her helplessness. Then the sense of shame and worthlessness that engulfed her as she realised that kindness had been used as bait to lure her into homosexuality. The kindness had disappeared, leaving sadism in its place. In Angie's mind now as she stood before the mirror, the word 'love' had become synonymous with bondage, fear, humiliation, guilt, and pain. A deep feeling of hopelessness engulfed her, as she re-experienced the betrayals. She felt so dirty; obviously she was very evil for such things to keep happening to her. Feelings of hatred for herself overwhelmed her.

Biting her lip to try to force herself to stop trembling, the burden and pain of living seemed to her to be greater than the fear of death. With trembling hand, she picked up the razor and rested it on her wrist. She shuddered, closed her eyes, and took a deep breath. At that moment, the door burst open, the stillness pierced by curses. The razor made a jagged little cut, then slipped to the floor, as Angie whirled around, her eyes wide with fear.

Cringing against the wall, unaware that she was holding her breath, she watched as Margaret exploded into action like an irate sergeant-major. In quick strides, she crossed the room, grabbed Angie by her hair and began to pull her towards the bed. The younger woman screamed in helpless pain as she was forced to the bed and then beaten. Finally, breathing heavily, Margaret stepped back looking satisfied, as Angie lay motionless, like a broken doll, her eyes staring blankly at the ceiling.

Margaret, now relaxed, reached into her purse and took out a pack of cigarettes. She lit one and with a sneer handed it to Angie. 'Burn yourself. Go on, burn yourself, you sack of useless rubbish!'

Angie began to weep like a little child. Her body shuddered with revulsion, as in obedience she took the cigarette and placed it on the soft, tender skin of her arm.

'That's it! Pay yourself off. Go on, do it again! And remember, if you want to kill yourself, go somewhere else. I don't want the blood from your lily-white skin dirtying up my carpet.'

Angie obeyed, and as the smell of burning flesh rose the short distance to her nostrils, she felt detached from what she was doing. She looked down at the burn marks on her arms, then over to the mirror, where its crack from top to bottom seemed to be screaming at her, 'Pay yourself off again!'

'What am I?', she thought to herself. 'A thing to be used, a piece of lemon to squeeze until all the juice is gone and only an empty husk remains?' Angie prayed for the first time since she was a little girl, 'God, you must be a sadist to make a world like this. Do me a favour, just let me die.' She rolled over, her back turned to Margaret, who was scraping sweet and sour sauce with her little finger from yesterday's Chinese take-away container. Curling up in a foetal position, Angie began to rock like a baby. Soon Margaret turned the light out and walked toward the bed.

6

Huss sat on the easy chair in Rick and Sheila's front room. A cup of coffee was on the floor next to him. The flat was neat, though simply furnished. What made it friendly was the abundance of green, leafy plants, and a combination of pictures and plaques on the wall. Some were the typical bingo prizes from Canvey Island, whilst others were nicely framed Bible verses with waterfalls and mountain scenes in the background. 'Actually, Huss, we want to talk to you,' Rick said.

Huss smiled. 'Shoot!'

'Well, you know you said that because you got Angie all messed up, that you were never going to marry? You know, penance for your sin and all that stuff. Well, what we were thinking was that decision was like a religious thing, you know, paying for your own sin. In Psalms, it says that God does not want penance from us.' Rick became quite excited as he realised that for the first time he was able to put biblical ideas into real words, that connected with Huss. 'Then, if Jesus died to pay the price of your sin, isn't it true that he sees you as clean? And if that is true, then why do you have to pay him off for messing up Angie?'

Before Huss could answer, Sheila spoke. 'See, Huss, I haven't really spoken to you about this subject since the night I exploded, and I need to share a few things with you. When it all happened, I hated you, as you know.

'But the crazy thing about it all was that Angie had been so insistent that she would remain pure until she met Mr Right, and now here she had not only gone and got herself pregnant, but she had had an abortion on top of it. Because she hadn't lived up to her dreams, she was being destroyed by it, and I hated you for that.

'I was concerned about Angie, so I went to her house to see her on Sunday. We went for a walk together; I really wanted to help her, but she was so distraught, it was like she was suddenly in another world where I couldn't reach her. I will never forget her saying there was no hope left, then turning and walking away from me. The sky had darkened for it had begun to rain. It seemed appropriate, because the tears were streaming down both of our faces, and we were lost in our own darkness. In my despair, I walked and walked, until in the end I didn't really know where I was. That was the night I became a believer.'

Sheila bowed her head, as though struggling to go on. Then looking up, her eyes moist with unshed tears, she continued, 'You know, when I spat at you? Well, I wanted to get you, I mean really get you. Well...' The tears began to spill over, and with effort, she continued, 'Well, the Friday I kicked you out, I rang up this guy who used to be a kneecap buster when the Krays were around and asked him how much it would cost to give you a skiing accident. I decided that on Monday morning, I was going to take out a loan from the Co-op and tell them it was for furniture. Then I was going to get you done up.'

Bursting into tears, she was unable to continue. Rick put his arm around her, then gently kissed her on the forehead.

Huss began to choke up and spoke with a quivering voice as his eyes welled up with tears. 'It's O.K., Sheila, honest. I was a dog. I deserved whatever I would have got.'

Sheila blew her nose, then continued. 'God used Angie's pain and my hatred for you to show me my real self. It wasn't a pretty picture. As I prayed, it was the blood of Jesus that set me free from my sin and my hatred. The exciting thing is that God not only completely forgave me, but he taught me to forgive you. Somehow, I know that God finds joy in forgiving us.'

All three fell silent. After some moments, Huss sat back in his chair, roughly wiped his eyes, and stared at the ceiling. He began to weep softly and, speaking hesitantly, said, 'You're right, Sheila; Angie was a good girl, she was a virgin when we met. But I messed her up. I can't forgive myself—and you are right, deep down I can't really accept that God has forgiven me. It's like he's forgiven me enough to let me go to heaven, but I still have to pay him back for messing up Angie.' Sobs shook his body, then, taking a deep breath, he squared his shoulders and collected himself. 'You see, it's not quite the way it seemed. Angie didn't give herself to me. I guess, really, if I am honest, I would have to say that I raped her. At the time, I didn't think that, but now as a believer, that is the only thing I can call it. Rape. I raped her.'

The words burst out of Sheila unbidden, 'Oh, my God!'

'It's horrible, isn't it? I deserve you to hate me, but I can't go on living a lie, especially when you've been so honest. You see, it seemed O.K. at the time. You know, we're fed this line that the girl always says no but she really wants it. Well, I believed it, and I actually thought I was doing her a favour. She trusted me, and then, after the abortion, I told her to shove off. I don't deserve to be forgiven. I made Angie what she is today. I'm nothing but scum.'

Huss shuddered, then whispered brokenly, 'Sheila, I'm sorry, I'm so sorry for what I did, but it's too late.'

Sheila, who was weeping, reached out to touch Huss's hand. 'No, Huss. It's not too late. What you did was terrible, but I know God would want you to forgive yourself. Feeling guilty can't help Angie. She needs you. If you accept God's forgiveness, and pray for Angie, you may find God will use you to help her find healing.' By now all three were weeping as God's love and forgiveness began to pour healing into their young, wounded lives.

7

Nick stood at the telephone kiosk on the corner of Stoke
Newington Church Street. As he dialled Roulla, a childlike excitement engulfed him. Roulla's father answered
the telephone. 'Oh, hi Mr Kyriacou, this is Nick
Thompson. May I speak to Androulla?'

'Yeah, sure Nick, hang on.'

Holding his hand over the mouthpiece, he shouted,
'Hey, Androulla! It's Nick.' As she bounded down the
stairs, her hand outstretched, he added, 'That kid's got
class. He's the only English person I know that can
pronounce Kyriacou correctly and he calls you
Androulla instead of Roulla. Maybe this kid can get you
to take that orange streak out of your hair.'

Giggling, she took the receiver, 'Hi! What's the head-
lines?'

'Roulla, I just want you to know that I love that
orange streak in your hair.'

Roulla laughed as she turned to look at her father who
was telling her Mum that that kid had class. She giggled
and spoke, 'If only you knew, if only you knew.'

'Roulla, look, don't get me wrong. I don't want to
spoil anything, but I've really got it for you.'

Roulla spoke softly, 'You're quite to the point, aren't
you.'

Nick answered, 'Well, I don't know how to put it, but

it's like since I became a believer, everything is different, you know?' Roulla felt a warmth in her heart as Nick continued.

'What I mean is, I really like you. Before, when I took a girl out, well, I was just interested in kissing and all that stuff. When I was praying this morning, it was almost like God was speaking to me about being pure. What I was wondering, like, was if we could be...you know, special friends? I really feel it is important not to rush things, you know, give you space to find out if you feel the same, and especially to find out if God wants us to become closer.'

Roulla held the telephone close to her face and whispered, 'Nick, what you just said is the most beautiful thing anyone has ever said to me.'

Nick felt like all his burdens had suddenly lifted like a cloud on a summer's morning. 'Roulla, I feel like something beautiful and sensitive was just set free within me. It really is because of Jesus. Oh, Roulla, even now, right now, I feel like Jesus is with us and that we are clean.'

Roulla sighed, 'I know, Nick. He's absolutely terrific!'

Nick suddenly felt an urgent need calling to be attended to, 'Look, I've got to go but I'll telephone you tomorrow evening. I feel like I can fly!'

Roulla laughed, 'I already am, my feet are hovering about twelve inches off the ground!'

Nick hung up and ran across the road into the pub, making straight for the toilets. Once there, he began to laugh at the sense of relief he was experiencing. Glancing around at all the graffiti on the toilet wall, he smiled, then took a pencil from his pocket and wrote, 'I'm a happy man because Jesus has set me free from all this rubbish on the wall! If you're reading this, think about what it could mean for you if you had a clean heart.' As he walked into the street, the idea came to his mind that he could get all the believers to go around writing gospel messages on toilet walls. Then for some strange reason he had a feeling that maybe that wasn't the best thing. It caused him a moment's confusion until he remembered Huss saying be careful not to let your feelings dominate how you live.

8

'Hey, Kenny, this is your friendly Goy. What's the head-lines?'

Kenny laughed as he sat on the stairs with the telephone balanced between his shoulder and his ear. He was working the Rubik cube and needed both hands to accomplish the impossible. With a sigh, he put it down, shifted the telephone to his other ear, then spoke, 'Nick, listen, I'm glad you rang. I wanted to ring you but thought maybe I shouldn't because of your dad.'

Nick interrupted, 'Man, I'm sick because of that. It ought never to have happened.'

'Don't worry about it. It's O.K. Listen, I was really touched because you cared. Smacking up those geezers was one thing, but...well anyway, I feel good about knowing you. In fact, I was thinking today that your religion is not like rituals and stuff that you have to do. Instead it's like it's in your veins and just happens naturally. I'm impressed. It's not for me, but I'm impressed.'

Nick looked out of the phone box to the railway track across from where he was standing. 'Thanks for saying that. My dad has a thing about Jews, but I never thought he would act like that. I've had a guts-ache ever since the other night. It must be really bad having that stuff all the time.'

Kenny shook his head, then picked up the Rubik cube, as he wrinkled his face. 'It's not all the time that you face prejudice, but yeah, knowing that it is always simmering below the surface, and can erupt for no apparent reason at any moment, is hard.'

A train had pulled into the station and slowed to a stop but no one got off. In a moment, it was moving again. Nick raised his voice over the background noise, 'What I was ringing for was to say I have a girlfriend.' It felt good just saying the words. 'We were wondering if you would like to come out with us? My sister Chrissy is going to come too. It wouldn't be like a blind date, but just to make up a foursome.'

'Hey, now you're speaking my language.'

'No, seriously, Kenny, you'll have to be sensitive not to try it on with Chrissy, 'cause she's all smashed up on the inside because of being messed about.'

'Hey man, I'm your actual personification of straightness.'

'Kenny, you need a shrink, straight up. You'd better get one quick before the Iron Lady takes them all off the National Health. Anyway, meet us tomorrow at Manor House Underground Station at about eight o'clock and we will take you to this Greek joint that Roulla's uncle owns. And I want you to meditate on this; this is a classy joint so no dancing on the tables!'

'Say no more. I will be there promptly at eight o'clock to share your repast.'

Nick hung up the telephone as another train was heading off into the distance. The rain had just increased to a steady drizzle as he stepped out of the kiosk. Putting up his collar, he hunched up his shoulders. Rounding the corner, he saw the 149 winding its way up Kingsland Road. Unconsciously, as the bus passed, he heaved a sigh of relief; it was not his father driving. Thinking of all the action that had recently passed through his life, he began to whistle softly to himself.

9

The Spartan Tavern Restaurant in Harringay buzzed with life. A Greek music group, pulsating with life, played as the patrons sat laughing and eating. The violin player, a dangerous-looking Greek whose long black hair swayed as he moved, walked around serenading the couples. His white shirt, unbuttoned to the centre of his chest, revealed a dark, matted forest of hair, whilst around his neck was a gold chain that flapped and twirled in synchronisation to its master's movement. Focusing his attention on attractive young females, he would lean over the table and play such heart-stoppers as 'Yesterday' and 'When a Man Loves a Woman'.

As they entered the busy restaurant, various waiters were moving to and fro delivering the most spectacular array of Greek dishes. Roulla's Uncle Stavros stood at the door, cheerfully greeting customers as they arrived. Stavros was short and overweight. Nearly bald, he had a full beard, as if to compensate. He wore gold rings on both hands. Often he would gallantly bow and kiss the hand of the ladies as they entered this arena of gourmet delight and sensuous sound. Everyone knew he was the owner and enjoyed the personal attention he gave them. Roulla had grown up in this atmosphere and so knew all the ins and outs, the untidy details, as well as the joys and triumphs of a successful family-owned business.

Nick was overwhelmed, as was Chrissy. They had both eaten kebab before, but always from a Turkish take-away. They had been to Chinese and occasionally to Indian restaurants, but never had they been in an atmosphere quite like this. Kenny, on the other hand, was completely at home, and felt himself soaking up the atmosphere.

Costas, the violin player, soon made his way to their table to do his number. As he gushed all over Chrissy, she flushed and began to squirm in embarrassment. Roulla, in a protective manner, leaned across the table, and spoke in a stage whisper to Chrissy, 'They say he shoots up steroids to make the hair on his chest grow.' The well-aimed Greek dart, shot at the Achilles heel, had done its damage. Costas turned away, uttering an otherwise unutterable Greek expression at Roulla. The group laughed heartily, mainly from relief, yet not loud enough to cause a scene.

Nick looked at Roulla, thinking how special she was. A combination of street wisdom and gentle sensitivity, she constantly amazed him. Roulla looked around the restaurant, then spoke to Nick, 'Let me introduce you to my auntie.'

The two stood up and, weaving their way between tables, made their way through to the kitchen. A short, plump woman was arranging food on a large stainless steel platter. 'Auntie!' Roulla called out, as they stood by the swinging doors.

'Androulla, my love. Do come in.' Auntie Maria, her face lighted by a smile, reached out to embrace Roulla, then kissed her on both cheeks.

'Auntie, this is my friend Nick.'

Nick stepped hesitantly forward, stretching out his hand. 'Hi, Mrs Fillipou. Androulla has told me a lot about you.'

'Nice boy, Androulla. And did you hear? He even pronounces my name properly.' Then, with a wink, she added, 'But remember, they are all devils inside!' Turning to take a good look at Roulla, her eyes widened with amazement. 'Whatever is that horrible orange in your hair?' Throwing her hands up in mock horror she continued. 'My heavens, if anybody in the village back home could see this! Nick, hmph. Well, at least it's a Greek name. Can't you tell her that she needs to get rid of this orange thing?'

Nick, who was almost blown away with the intensity of all the words that had suddenly belted forth, blurted out the first thing that came to his head. 'Mrs Fillipou, do you know you and your cousin look so much alike! You could be sisters.'

'Cousin? I'm her auntie.'

'Nooo. I'm sorry, but I can't believe it. Why, you look so young, surely you can't be her aunt.'

'I like this boy, Androulla. I like this boy, he has insight. Go on, take him back inside.'

As they turned to leave, Nick stopped, reached out and kissed Auntie Maria's hand, who, smiling, returned to her work.

Walking back to their table, Roulla looked in awe at Nick. 'How come you can pronounce these Greek names so perfectly?'

Nick smiled and shrugged his shoulders. 'Is Nick really a Greek name?'

'Kind of. Actually it's Nickos,' she replied.

Nick paused, narrowing his eyes as though making an important decision. Looking into Roulla's dark brown, doe-like eyes, he asked, 'Will you call me that when we're on our own?'

Stunned, Roulla looked around the restaurant. All her life she had run away from being Greek. In spite of everything she did to belong, even though she had been born in England, somehow she always felt as if she was a stranger. Yet in Cyprus she was considered a foreigner, because in essence she was a Londoner. Now, here was

47

an English fellow making her feel good about being Greek.

When Nick and Roulla returned to the table, it was evident that Kenny and Chrissy had been deep in a very serious conversation. Chrissy's eyes were filled with tears and Kenny was sitting with a strange look on his face. Kenny spoke, 'I'm sorry, I didn't mean to spoil the evening by talking about me and all my problems.'

Chrissy turned to Nick and Roulla, tears streaming down her cheeks. 'I can't stand all the hate and fear in this city. Do you know what they did to Kenny when he was a little boy? Some English kids got him down in the street and smeared rancid pig-fat all over his face and hair. He was so scared that he wouldn't go home until late that night. Why, Nick? Why? If Jesus is who you say he is, then why would a little kid be told it was his fault because the Jews killed Jesus?'

Roulla reached out her hand and squeezed Chrissy's hand. Kenny frowned, 'I'm sorry, I shouldn't have spoken about it, Chrissy. I didn't realise it would upset you so.' He was amazed that one with such great beauty could also have a depth of compassion that would enable her to agonise over the pain of a little Jewish boy. He felt a bit guilty that he had joked with Nick about trying to get off with her. As he looked around the table, he felt a growing sense both of warmth and confusion as he considered this new group of friends whose lives he had invaded.

'Oh, good grief!' Roulla put her hand over her mouth in alarm. 'Oh, Kenny, we've brought you here to this restaurant and they have pork in the kitchen.'

Nick made a face and turned away, angry with himself. 'Why didn't I think of that? Oh man, I'm really sorry.'

'Hey, it's O.K. No, really. It's O.K.,' Kenny replied, trying to reassure them. 'I've ordered fish. Anyway, I'm not kosher, so I just eat fish when I'm in places like this.'

Just then, the food arrived, creating a welcome diversion.

As the group happily tucked into their meal, a tall Greek in his early forties walked up to their table. 'Nick, Chrissy, I didn't know you came here.' Demetrious lived two doors down from Nick and was married to an English girl. He nodded at Kenny and Roulla, then continued, 'Must be all these Greek lessons I've been giving him. Twice this week he's come around, spent nearly an hour learning how to pronounce Greek people's names. Anyway, you lot, enjoy yourselves.'

Nick, flushed, feeling as if he had been discovered with his hand in the biscuit tin, responded in a subdued voice, 'Yeah, see ya.'

Roulla looked at Nick with a deep appreciation for his wanting to say the right thing when meeting her relatives, then leaned over and whispered in his ear, 'Nickos, I think you have some Greek blood in you.' As he smiled, looking a bit like the cat who ate the canary, she raised her eyebrows and added, 'Maybe some Irish too!'

10

Tuesday evening with Kenny and Chrissy along was a new experience for the group. There was a certain amount of nervousness as everyone wanted to make the visitors welcome without patronising or overdoing it. For Chrissy and Kenny, the experience seemed destined to bring them closer for, although they felt welcome, it was still a 'them-and-us' situation, believers and non-believers.

The meeting began when Huss asked Kenny to share some of his feelings, as Nick had given them such a big build-up about his Jewish friend. Kenny, feeling nervous, licked his lips as he looked around the table. Seeing everyone lean forward, as though what he had to say was very important, gave him a feeling of confidence. Clearing his throat, he began, 'Well, what can I say? I feel just a little bit like I am on stage.'

'No, mate,' Nick laughed, 'you're not on stage, you're on trial!'

Kenny looked at Nick and didn't smile. 'Actually, we have often been on trial before your lot.'

Nick looked embarrassed. 'I'm sorry, man. I didn't mean it like that. That was stupid of me.'

Kenny smiled 'O.K. I guess I'm a bit on the defensive. I didn't mean to wind you up. Let me say that ever since I was a child, I felt insecure around Christians, Gentiles, whatever. Sometimes I just want to block them out of my mind, like they don't exist. For me, security was in my home, my family. I can't explain it but being Jewish sort of encompasses everything, from how we think, to how we prepare our food. It is our culture and our religion, influencing our everyday life, giving us our traditions, which are a part of us. You don't think it through or question whether it is true or false. You're just Jewish.'

Rick spoke. 'Don't you ever have doubts? Or even wonder about other religions?'

Kenny looked serious. 'This may sound strange to you, but although there have been debates, I have never thought about alternatives. Oh, I question God about why we have a sick world but that part of my mind is completely different from Sabbath day preparations or our various holidays. It is like I ask questions, but only within the boundaries of my religion. You know what I mean?'

Huss frowned. 'Nick told us about the agro you've had because of being Jewish. How do you feel deep inside of you about that?'

Kenny raised his eyebrows. 'Do you really want me to be totally honest?'

Chrissy smiled. 'Give it to them. Totally.'

'Well, it's like this. I want the nation of Israel to exist, with us, the Jews, having the machine guns. For the first time since King David's day, Jews are not all being pushed around. When Israel does stuff like rescue hostages, or knock off terrorists, I love it. I feel good. It's like, they are my flag, my pride.' He looked down at the table, then squared his shoulders, lifted his head and narrowed his eyes, his jaw set as he faced the group.

'But then over here, it's different. I just want as many of our lot as possible to get smart, then go into politics, law, or some profession. The rest need to get into money and buy everything in sight. Buy out the newspapers, the whole bag so we can influence and even form public opinion in a positive way. Like, it's how we protect ourselves.'

'That is interesting.' Roulla slowly emphasised each word, shaking her head at the same time. 'O.K., don't get me wrong, but is that why Jews are so keen on making money? So they can control things?'

Kenny shook his head. 'It's protection we're concerned about, not aggression. That honestly is the truth. Sure, there are Jewish monsters like anywhere else, but the obsession with achievement and money is purely a way of building a protective coating around ourselves.'

Nick spoke. 'You know, Kenny, knowing you has taught me so much. I've seen prejudice, and all that, but never from the perspective of the one being hurt. After our experience on the train, well, it's kinda strange, but it's like I feel a link with you, even a responsibility to protect you. Does that offend you?'

Kenny sighed, slowly moved his head back and stared at the ceiling. 'It's hard to explain. You see, part of me feels accepted by you, and yet, a part of me, please don't misunderstand this, but a part of me is frightened of you. I feel like if I really let myself go and totally trust you, who will protect me if you turn against me? Then another part of me feels embarrassed, because you were only one bloke on that train, yet you stood up against that gang when there was nothing you could get out of it, except maybe being beaten up.'

Nick felt a mixture of guilt and excitement wash over him, yet wished he only felt guilt as he wanted to escape the bother boy image. 'Ahh, it was just luck that they ran away.'

'Hmm. No, don't tell me it was luck. I saw your face. So did they. Your face said "I'll go all the way, I will destroy." But even now being modest puts you in a position of strength. That makes me feel weak.'

Sheila deftly changed the subject. 'What do you think, Kenny, about our being believers in Jesus and all that?'

'It's weird. I can't explain it properly but I told Nick that I was really impressed but that it is not for me. But, as I think about it, that's not the whole truth. You see, it has made me want to take your honesty and love, if you will, and inject it into my religion. You make me want to be a better Jew.'

Nick looked at Roulla, who smiled a knowing kind of smile. 'But, what if what you believe is not true? You know, what if it is rather simply a right or wrong situation?

'See, you used the word "simply" because for you it is simple. For me nothing is simple, like right or wrong. To me, tradition makes up ninety per cent of what my life is all about. I don't think in terms of this is right and this is wrong.

'O.K. We are really being honest, right? Well, my biggest problem...' Pausing for effect, Kenny looked at Chrissy, '...is that I really like you, Chrissy, and that is making me nervous, because I am a Jew and you are a Christian.'

Chrissy quickly snapped back. 'I'm not a Christian! I'm nothing.' Her angry reaction surprised even herself, but she was stunned by Kenny's public statement about his interest in her. She didn't know whether to laugh or to cry. She also felt confused and frightened, for, since the evening at the Greek restaurant, she no longer had a tight grip on her emotions.

She tossed her head, then spoke nervously, preceded by a throat-clearing cough. 'Actually, I don't think it matters what religion you have as long as you are good to people. Really, I wouldn't mind becoming Jewish if it came down to it.'

Nick was feeling confused. This Tuesday night had been the time when he had hoped Kenny would become a Christian. Instead, it was Kenny who was converting his own sister.

Huss entered the conversation. 'I was born a Muslim. I felt like you did, Kenny, about religion and the home. But it was like, for me, well, it was more something I did; because it was such a part of our culture and home, I accepted it without question, yet never gave my heart to it. It was more an outside influence.' He looked at Sheila and Rick, sighed, then continued. 'Inside I was something else. Actually, I was all screwed up, but then when Jesus came into my life, I got unscrewed.'

Kenny nodded. 'That's nice. I am really happy for you. If doing what you did was what you had to do to get unscrewed, if you will excuse my French, then do it. But I can't see things as you do. You think, like, well, that Jesus is the only way. Yes?'

Roulla shook her head, smiling at Kenny. 'Actually, you're too hot to handle! Honest, we can't answer you because what we've got, in your eyes, is O.K. for us, but not for you. It just can't be answered.'

Kenny sat up straight, feeling like he had won a debate. Holding both palms upwards, he shrugged, 'But I am just being honest.'

Roulla leaned forward, her elbows on the table, and speaking intently, said, 'And I am being honest when I say this on behalf of all of us. We love you, man, and want to be your friend, no matter how much we ever disagree.'

Nick nodded his head. 'Yeah. That's right, man.' Then, looking at his sister, he frowned, immediately beginning to worry about her.

11

Sheila lay flat on her back on the soft carpet in her front room, her legs suspended on the couch. In the background the powerful lyrics of Keith Green's music filled the air. It was Huss that had turned Rick and herself onto his music. The words 'like waking up from a long bad dream' hung in the air. Quietly she began to speak.

'Oh Jesus, I love you. It's so good to be in the process of being set free. All those years, I walked in darkness. In spite of all I did to fill life with joy and laughter, it was all so hollow, so empty.' She laughed a lilting laugh. 'Now I am alive and free.'

She jumped when the jarring ring of the telephone invaded her sanctuary. Rolling over to turn the music down, but still relaxed on the floor, she picked up the receiver.

'Hello.'

'Sheila, is that you? It's Angie. Long time and all that.'

Adrenalin shot through Sheila's body, and she quickly jumped up to turn the music off.

'How's things going with you and Rick?'

Sheila's heart overflowed in a silent prayer, as she heard her friend's voice.

'Good, Angie, good. We've become believers, and we got married! It's like being a different person.'

Angie spoke almost in a whisper. 'That's nice, Sheila, really nice.'

'Oh Angie, it's so good to hear your voice. When are you going to come and see me?'

'Oh, sometime. I'm kinda busy.'

'Angie, I miss you so much. It's horrible not being able to see you any more. Where do you live? I could come around and visit you.'

'Oh, I'm not calling from the flat. I'm in a call box.'

'That's O.K. I could meet you somewhere?'

'Ah, you don't want to know me now.' She paused, sighed, then spoke again. 'You see, I'm in trouble, you know, really in it. The ride is too painful, and so I'm thinking about getting off.' Her laugh sounded shrill, and false. 'Yeah, do meself in, or something. You know?'

'Oh, Angie. Please let me see you. I love you.'

'I know all about love. I've had my fill of it. So don't tell me you love me! Hmph! If you knew about me, you would be running so fast the other way. So don't say that.' Angie spoke bitterly.

Sheila responded gently. 'You mean, knowing about you being gay?'

Angie spoke with disbelief, 'You know? And you don't hate me?'

'Oh, Angie.' Sheila began to cry. 'I love you. I know you got into this mess because you were so hurt. How I wish I was with you right now. I'm your friend, remember? How could I hate you?'

Angie began to cry too. 'I hate myself. I just thought you wouldn't want me, like, because I'm a Lesbo.'

'Please don't say that. You're precious to me, nothing you can do will ever change that.'

'Oh, Sheila, I'm so unhappy, so lonely, so lost. I've got nobody, except this bird I'm living with. She's really a monster but I've got nowhere else to go.'

'Oh yes, you do!' Sheila spoke almost violently.

'Angie, come here. We love you. I threw Huss out after your abortion, so we have a room waiting just for you.'

'I don't know...' Angie sounded fearful.

'Please, you can come right now. You don't even need to go back where you're living. You can share my things.'

'I'm afraid. I don't know if I can do it.'

'Rick is here. He can pick you up.' Turning towards the kitchen, she called, 'Rick, come quick, it's Angie!'

As Rick came into the room, Sheila was finding out where Angie was. 'O.K., O.K., Kilburn Lane by the Odeon. Rick's coming right away, but stay on the phone with me until he gets there.'

Angie stood in the phone box weeping like a child. It was almost too much to believe that after all the rejection and pain she had been through, that there might be a haven where she would be safe.

Sheila and Angie stayed on the telephone until Rick arrived. As Sheila hung up, she fell down on her knees, the tears streaming down her face, 'Thank you, Lord. O Lord Jesus, thank you for bringing Angie back into our life. Bless her, Lord, and free her from the fear that is destroying her.'

Rising to her feet, she quickly began to prepare the spare room for their special guest. She placed a vase with some flowers on the bureau, and put Rick's reading lamp, from their own bedroom, on the little bedside table. Getting her favourite picture of a shepherd reaching down to rescue the lost sheep, she smiled as she hung it on the wall. Then she took the blue curtains with ruffles on them from their own bedroom, and exchanged them with the plain ones in the guest room. As she scurried around doing little things to make Angie feel at home she felt a deep sense of joy.

'O Jesus,' she said, 'I would never have been like this before, but it's like you want to give to Angie and you're doing it through me. Lord, let her find peace in this home.'

She opened a little box of lavender-scented soap and laid it on a clean towel at the foot of the bed. It was almost the finishing touch but then Sheila remembered something. Getting her own Bible, she placed it tenderly on Angie's pillow, then prayed, 'Jesus, make your Word come alive to Angie.'

She had barely finished when she heard the key in the door. Eagerly, she ran into the hall, and then, almost as if she had been struck, she reeled back against the wall. Could this broken person, barely recognisable, who stood before her really be Angie?

Angie stood hesitantly in the doorway, fear and defiance written across her face. Recovering, Sheila smiled, stretched out her arms, and walked towards her. 'Welcome home, Angie. We love you. This is your place, for ever if you want it to be.'

At this, Angie's defences were broken down, and she slumped into Sheila's arms and sobbed like a baby. In the stillness, a bond grew between the two girls. Rick stood on and watched, his eyes misted with unshed tears.

Sheila smiled lovingly, stepping back. Tenderly she wiped the tears from Angie's face. 'Come with me.' Taking Angie's hand, she led her to the guest room. Sunlight poured cheerfully through the frilly curtains, seeming to fall directly on the picture of the lamb with the verse, 'Come unto me, all you who have heavy burdens, and I will give you rest.' The scent from the soap had begun to permeate the air, creating a freshness. But it was another deeper fragrance pouring into the room, that touched Angie to the depth of her being. It was the fragrance of Jesus flowing from one wounded soul to another.

'Sheila, it's beautiful.' Angie began to cry again.

Sheila reached out and held Angie in a comforting embrace. 'It's your special place now. Welcome.'

12

Nick smashed his fist against the wall and then recoiled in agony. It seemed all wrong that life, which was so beautiful last week, should now be so unbearable. On his lunch hour, he picked up the telephone and dialled the Social Security office where Huss worked.

'Listen, man, I'm in a bad way. I really am. I've got to talk. Can we get together?'

'Of course. How about tonight, say about six-thirty?'

'All right, but let's go somewhere different. You know, somewhere away from it all.'

'O.K. Let's meet at Westminster Bridge on the south side.'

Nick hung up the telephone and walked into the front room, where Chrissy was reading a magazine. 'Are you going out with Kenny now?'

Chrissy lowered the magazine. 'I don't know, but we feel close. I'm not ready for anything heavy. It's strange, though, because when I heard about those dudes on the train, I really got angry. I wanted revenge, like, nuke the whole of Whitechapel to make sure we got them. I guess that has affected my emotions, making me softer towards him. You know?'

Nick smiled, though inwardly he was in agony. He looked at his watch, sighed, it would be three more hours before he could see Huss.

Looking at Chrissy, he felt a feeling of compassion steal over him. She had been so alone in her pain. He nodded and then spoke. 'I don't think I've ever said this to you, you know, 'cause you're my sister, but I love you. I really do.'

Chrissy smiled. 'I love you too. I'm sorry I called your friends weird, they're not. They're really nice people, and I enjoyed going to your meeting.'

Three hours later, Nick was walking up and down by the south side of Westminster Bridge. Just over the river were Big Ben and the Houses of Parliament. People in all sorts of shapes, sizes and fashions made their way in either direction over the bridge. There were American tourists, cameras around their necks, looking enthusiastic about everything, and loaded down with plastic bags full of souvenirs. Nick liked the Americans. A trifle naive as a race, but truly a generous people, he thought to himself. His father hated America and her people. Nick had never understood why, except that his father was convinced the Jews ran the country. As he was pondering, he saw Huss making his way over the bridge from the north side. He respected Huss for he had his act together, and really seemed to know so much about the Bible.

'Hey, man! What's happening?'

As Huss stretched out his hand, Nick thought, 'Huss is always shaking people's hands, like it's his trademark, or something.'

Huss motioned, 'Look down there by the river. It's quiet and there's no one down there. We can be private.'

An old lady with a rusty, bent pram slowly made her way towards them. Her faded dress was ragged and dirty and she wore one sock and a worn-out pair of men's shoes. Varicose veins covered her legs giving them the appearance of a railway map. Her hair, filthy and matted, was covered by a ragged scarf. As she walked, she muttered to herself. Occasionally stopping to shout directions at the traffic, she looked like a scarecrow that had come untied and was flapping in the wind.

The two reached a quiet spot overlooking a low wall as the River Thames flowed beneath them.

'Do you want to get straight into it, Nick?'

Nick sighed, 'Yeah, I suppose so. Well, it's all to do with Roulla. But it's more than that.'

Huss smiled. 'I've seen you two getting closer. It's nice, man. She's a lovely person.'

Nick looked tense and frustrated. 'I guess that's part of the problem. See, before I was a believer, I really got about quite a bit, you know, with different girls. But when I became a believer, obviously that had to stop.'

Nick paused, turned his back to the river, and, frowning, looked up at the sky. 'Well, I still do it in my mind.' He closed his eyes. 'See, the problem is, man, I'm thinking about Roulla in that way. It makes me feel sick. Oh, God, I feel like it's defiling her inside my head. It's like everything inside of me wants to do the right thing. Why, I can even be memorising Bible verses and then, bang, the feeling comes and I'm zapped.' He looked back at the river, then turned and looked back at Huss. 'The other thing is... Are you still listening?'

'Yeah, yeah, of course I'm listening.' Huss turned, facing Nick.

'Well, the thing that really scares me is, what if I try it on with Roulla? Like, I could never live with myself.'

Huss watched silently as a small flock of pigeons flew within thirty feet of them. The groaning sound of traffic from Westminster Bridge seemed to find an echo in their souls. A groaning because of an unexplainable and totally irrational force that dwelt within the sanctuary of their innermost self.

Huss spoke quietly. 'It would be easier if sex didn't exist, but then God made it as something beautiful. We not only got it all messed up but we've made it incredibly selfish.'

Nick looked surprised. 'Do you mean you also struggle with this feeling?' When Huss nodded his head, Nick asked, 'Why doesn't God take the feelings away from the believer and then give them back when we get married?'

Huss laughed. 'Nick, you are so practical. I don't know. But there is something you are going to have to get inside your head. If you touch Roulla, you will damage her, but you are also going to damage yourself, and any future the two of you might have together will start out on a negative note.'

He sighed deeply. 'Even if you somehow think that she is giving you the come-on, you mustn't touch her. Love means you have got to protect her, especially from yourself.'

Nick turned again and looked at the sky. 'Man, that is heavy.' He paused. 'Heavy.'

Huss smiled. 'You're right. Life is not all happy days and Bible studies. Life is made up of choices. This is crude but you are going to have to choose to sacrifice all sexual desires in your life. You've got to say, if Jesus sacrificed everything for me to take the punishment for my sin, then I've got to be willing to sacrifice my instincts for this girl that I love.'

Huss took his comb out of his pocket and nervously began to scratch the wall.

'Huss, where did you get all of this stuff from? I mean, it's like you're a shrink and a priest all wrapped up in one.'

Huss smiled. 'Let's just say I've learned the hard way. Listen, let's make a pact, right here. We will call it the Thames Never Touch pact.' Huss picked up a nail and scratched the initials TNT onto the wall. 'So as of now we are going to pray for each other in this area, O.K.?'

Nick was almost light-headed. 'Right on. I feel really good about this. I really do. I don't feel so alone with this problem any more.'

13

Kenny and Chrissy walked companionably through the crowded street-market stalls of Petticoat Lane. All about them was an almost violent concoction of sights, colours, and sounds. Cockney Pakistanis selling silver-plated cups and dishes, competed in volume with the leather-coated merchants almost dragging people to their stalls. There was a riot of colour, as all types of clothing flapped in the wind, whilst dinner services and never-die batteries seemed almost to fly through the air, as they changed hands. In some places, music belted out, mingling with a cacophony of sounds that was almost deafening, while the smell of fried onions, hot dogs and hamburgers hung in the air. Kenny was just as much at home here as he was in the up-market Greek restaurant. Amidst the confusion, Chrissy was able to purchase a blouse and several yards of material for her mother. That completed, they decided that it was all a little too hectic, so made their way through the back streets down toward St Catherine's dock, just east of Tower Bridge. The contrast from the Lane was enormous. Sensing the peacefulness of the atmosphere, Chrissy placed her plastic bag on the wall and then stood looking out towards the river. Kenny stood beside her and, after a moment, quietly placed his arms around her.

Chrissy responded like a flash, throwing off his arms

and shouting, 'Don't touch me!' She sneered, 'You're like all the rest, aren't you? Just looking for what you can get.'

A look of pain crossed his face. Looking at the ground, he spoke softly. 'I'm sorry. I guess I imagined you cared more about me than you do. Please don't be angry.'

Surprised, Chrissy asked, 'Do you think that caring has to involve touching? Surely caring is much deeper than just taking, just pleasing one's self?'

'That's what I meant. If you cared for me, then you would want to give me physical pleasure.'

'Oh no you don't! Don't think I haven't heard that line before. What about you giving to me? If I don't want sexual involvement, then if you really cared, you wouldn't try to put one over on me.'

She picked up her plastic bag and began to walk away. Stunned, Kenny watched her, then, shaking his head, ran up to her. 'Hey lady, may I walk with you?' She smiled at him and, together, they made their way west the short distance towards the Tower of London. As they walked, they felt a combination of joy and confusion. For each of them the recipe was made up of different ingredients. For Chrissy, it was pleasure that Kenny had come after her, in spite of her refusing his physical advances, mixed with the fear of allowing herself to become emotionally involved.

Kenny realised that in going after Chrissy, he had already made an important decision. That decision was that he would seek to win Chrissy for himself, no matter what the cost. It brought a feeling of exhilaration, but then he seemed to see his family standing in a circle around him. He could see his father's look of disappointment, his lips crying out, 'Why?' His mother, her eyes rolling, looked like she was going to faint. He heard his brothers accusing him, fingers pointing in slow motion against him, while his sisters with their hands over their ears, and their eyes closed, were chanting, 'No, Kenny! No, Kenny!' The word 'assimilation' seemed to echo from the Jewish Boy's Club, and out onto the streets. The Torah was open and his rabbi was reading, 'You shall not take to yourselves wives of the daughters of the Gentiles.' Then six million faces, gaunt and malnourished, appeared on the screen of his mind. They were peering through barbed-wired fences and in an eerie voice calling his name. He stopped in the street, turned and looked at Chrissy. Her eyes seemed so vulnerable today. The quick intelligent look had been traded in for a look that made him think of a Jewish mother. A look of knowing yet caring. But also a look that revealed an uncertainty of what lay ahead, whether she would be struck, or given a plate of potato latkis.

'Chrissy, I have never met anyone like you. I respect your not wanting me to touch you, but I want you to know that I'm not going to just fade out of your life. My mug may not be much, but you're going to be seeing a lot of it.'

14

Chrissy picked up the telephone on the first ring. Roulla was on the other end. Chrissy liked Roulla. In spite of being a believer, she was real and seemed to accept people as they were.

Roulla spoke. 'Hi! How's it all going down there in Charm City?'

Chrissy answered with a smile, 'As usual. My Dad is still ill after the Conservative Party political broadcast last night. This must be the only house in London where anyone thinks Margaret Thatcher is a "leftie".'

Roulla laughed. 'Hey! She's a good woman. I mean, after all, she does the work of two men. Laurel and Hardy maybe, but still two men.'

Chrissy laughed. 'Oh! Here comes Nick. You should see him with his make-up off! Whew! Let me tell you, it's really quite awful.'

Nick grabbed the phone. 'Sorry, Roulla, Chrissy has gone off her head. She was watching the Muppets. Sad, but she has this thing for Kermit, and it unnerves her.'

Roulla laughed, then changed the course of the conversation. 'And how is Nickos today?'

Her voice communicated a sensitivity that slew Nick. He replied, 'I love it when you call me that.'

'Then I shall have to make sure that is what I always call you. Hey, I have wonderful news. Angie is staying with Rick and Sheila. Huss knows about it and he is hoping to be able to see her soon. We should pray for them, that somehow it will all work out.'

'That is great! But maybe we should just pray for them right now, on the phone,' Nick responded. 'It isn't going to be easy for either of them.'

Nick then prayed that God would guide Huss in what to say, and that he would also reveal to Angie the wonder of his love for her. As they finished praying, Nick and Roulla sensed a strengthening of the bond between them.

'You know, Nick, my greatest desire is to carry God's love to others. It must be so exciting to be used by God to bring healing into the life of someone who has been wounded.'

'Yeah. The thing is, there are wounded people all around us who need to be loved. You could even say we live in a wounded city, with countless numbers who need God's love. Maybe God will use us to touch them, but I am sure if he does, it will be costly.'

The two chatted for a while longer, then Nick said, 'Actually, I need to see you. Can we get together today?'

Roulla smiled. She loved his spontaneous approach to life. Roulla responded by singing the first line of the old Four Tops record, 'I'll be there with arms reaching out for you.'

Nick chuckled, 'How would you East End women ever function without script writers? O.K., how about—' he paused—'right now at Newington Green?'

Roulla looked at her watch, 'I need an hour and I'll be there.'

'O.K. See ya.'

Nick sat waiting on a park bench in the little garden at the centre of Newington Green. He loved it here. It would be an overstatement to call it peaceful but it was so green and fresh that it made him think of an oasis. Roulla came through the gate and walked carefully across the green so as to avoid the dogs' mess. She smiled at the fleeting impression that she was gingerly walking across a minefield. Seeing her, Nick rose and walked slowly towards her. Meeting on the grass, they reached out and touched each other's hands.

'Roulla, your hair! The orange tuft! It's gone! Whatever happened?'

Roulla looked shyly down at the grass, then deep into Nick's eyes. 'I always struggled with being Greek, you know, being different from everyone else. I so wanted to be accepted and I thought that if I did something like put that streak in my hair, then I wouldn't look Greek, and then I wouldn't feel like a misfit. Well, knowing you has made it O.K. for me to be Greek. I can just be me.'

At her words, Nick stood tall, his chest expanded with the pleasing sensation that he had just done something very special for the one he loved. 'I'm glad,' he smiled. Then reaching into his pocket, he brought out a small plastic bag. 'Here, it's something I got for you.'

She opened it carefully, as if it were some ancient treasure. Inside was a little leather purse, and engraved on the outside in gold letters was the name 'Androulla'.

Tears filled her eyes. 'I guess now I really am Greek. No more Roulla, and no more orange tuft.'

Nick took her hand in his as he faced her. 'Androulla, I love you. It is Androulla, the Greek, who I want to marry one day. I want to spend the rest of my life with you.'

'Harry, this is Charlie Watson. Look, mate, I don't want to stick my nose into your business at home and all that, but your kid, Chrissy, was down the Lane with a Yid on Sunday, then they took a long stroll together. It's up to you how you run your family but if it was up to me, I'd bust the slimy little Jew boy's legs. I thought you would want to know. Also, we can find out who he is without bringing her into it. In fact, Sunshine, just give me the word and we'll make sure that he never sees her again.'

15

Huss looked at himself in the mirror. His hair, short on the top and sides, was growing into a longer length hanging over the back of his collar. He realised now how unimportant his ego was compared to before he was a believer. In those days the streets had been a stage; a place to compete for the eyes of young women. Now, he saw the streets as a melting pot where wounded people spilled out of their homes and offices, the majority of whom wandered aimlessly through life, looking for something or somebody to fill that inward sense of void that gnaws away at the soul with insatiable greed.

Turning from the mirror, he slipped to his knees, his own soul in agony. 'Lord, help me. I know it's right to see Angie, but I just don't know what to say. Lord, help her to listen, and to see the change in me. Oh, comfort her heart, and bring her into your peace.'

Angie had borrowed some of Sheila's clothes, which made her feel feminine again. She wore a green blouse with long sleeves to cover up the burn marks, and green leggings. In the two weeks that Angie had been with them, her hair had grown a little. It was still extremely short, but with special treatment had regained a bit of its life. Now, after applying some make-up, she turned to Sheila.

'How do I look, Sheila? I don't want him to pity me.'

Sheila smiled, 'I doubt if he would pity you. You look quite attractive. A bit pale and thin but, nonetheless, still attractive.'

Rick walked downstairs to meet Huss before he came to the flat. It had begun to rain and the greyish-black streets reflected the light off the pavement, giving an almost surreal view to the area. As cars moved along, the sound of tyres on the wet road seemed to create a hissing noise in the background. A tremendous argument was going on in one of the nearby flats. Outside, a neighbour was screaming through the letter-box that if they did not quiet down, the police would come and take them away. The noise continued, with the neighbour becoming as loud and abusive as the warring parties. Rick was immune to this activity.

He smiled as he remembered the day some believers, who were friends of Huss, came from Bromley in Kent and how the area had blown them away. He remembered laughing as one girl asked if the water was safe to drink and how terrified she looked when Sheila had said, 'The water is O.K. but for goodness' sake don't breathe the air!' Then, on top of that, the Irish bloke upstairs threw his telly out of the window because, when he was watching football, the picture had gone all wonky.

Rick felt secure around here and, actually, felt lost when he travelled south of the Thames. A visit to the country left him feeling totally insecure because everything was so unfamiliar to him. As he philosophised on the destiny of the inner city, Huss turned the corner and almost bumped into him. Huss looked nervous, and seemed to be carrying the world on his shoulders.

'Listen, man, we thought it best that I meet you down here and see how you want to do this. You know, Angie is really different. I don't think she will be too excited to see you.' Huss reached his hand out and placed it on Rick's shoulder.

'Thanks, Rick. I'd love to see everything turn out like in the movies, but I guess I can only expect agro.'

Rick looked in the direction of the neighbour who was now going absolutely bananas, shouting through the letter-box that he knew they were illegal aliens and he was going to get the old Bill round and get them sent back to the jungle where they belonged.

Rick smiled at Huss, trying to relax the tension. 'Classy neighbourhood, this. Rumour is Charles and Di are thinking of buying a pad around here.'

As the door opened, Angie remained firmly entrenched on the couch.

'Come in, Huss. I see Rick found you.' Sheila smiled encouragingly, 'Angie is in the other room. Come on in.'

As the three walked into the room, Angie lifted her head as if ready to do battle. Her legs were crossed and the one moved gently back and forth, while her arms remained folded across her body. Her jaw was firm, and her eyes were narrowed in a defiant look.

Huss crossed the room, extending his hand. 'Hi, Angie.'

Not a muscle moved in her body, as she looked coldly at Huss. Then, turning to Sheila, she smiled and asked, 'Shall I make us all some tea?'

'Oh no, darling, you just sit and relax. I'll have it ready in no time,' Sheila responded as she almost ran out to the kitchen.

Huss and Rick took a seat and made some small talk until Sheila returned with a tray holding a teapot, two cups, milk and sugar, and a plate of biscuits. 'Angie, do be a love and pour the tea. Rick and I have to run off for a while. We promised to visit one of the old dears down the road.'

Silently, Angie poured the tea, setting a cup for Huss at the end of the table. Picking up her cup, she stirred some sugar into it, then sat back, leaning her head on the couch. 'I have absolutely nothing to say to you. I only agreed to see you because it made Sheila happy. So, if you have anything to say, then say it, and get on your bike.'

'I can understand your feelings, Angie, and I respect them. I—ah—wanted to talk to you. Like—ah—Sheila promised to arrange it for me.' Although Huss had realised it would be hard, he had not realised how bitter Angie would be, and he found it difficult to get into his carefully planned speech.

'I'm sorry you're upset.' At this, Angie made a face as if bored.

'It's taken me some time, but God is showing me how incredibly selfish I was. You see, you were different from the other girls. You were, well, innocent. I guess that was a challenge to me. I really liked you and then when I realised you felt the same, I, ah—Well, when we went to Epping Forest that day, I had the idea that you really wanted it, just as much as me.'

Angie clenched her teeth and, frowning, glared at Huss, then turned away from him in disgust.

'I know, I deserve your hate.' Huss bowed his head, as though unable to continue. Then, clearing his throat, he went on. 'You see, I had been fed a line, that if a girl says no, she really means yes. In my arrogance, I believed that. Then, as you resisted me, it was like a strange feeling swept over me, that I had to conquer you. As I took you... No. Rape. I have to call it what it is. When I raped you, I felt so powerful, like I was invincible. I was in total control and, well, it made me feel a man.'

At that, Angie exploded. 'A man! What kind of a man? Why, even animals don't stoop so low as rape.' Standing up, she walked to the window, 'Do you mean you have the arrogance to come to tell me that? That raping me made you feel like a man?' Turning, she was surprised to see Huss with his head bowed and his shoulders shaking.

72

Without looking up, he answered. 'No, that is not what I wanted to tell you.' He took out his handkerchief and blew his nose. Then looking at her, the tears still in his eyes, he went on. 'After your abortion, Sheila went wild. When Rick told me to leave and not to bother to come back, I felt like I had lost something important. Why, Rick and Sheila had been my mates for as long as I could remember. I really couldn't understand why Sheila had gone off her head. In the following weeks, I did a lot of thinking. God began to show me what a wretch I was, how deserving of punishment. I realised for the first time that I loved you and needed you.'

'Love?' Angie burst out. 'You don't know the meaning of love. To you, it is nothing more than satisfying your own ego. Don't you talk to me of love.'

'I'm sorry. I'm sure you're right. I tossed you aside without any thought and it was wrong. What I am trying to say is that God has shown me how I have wounded you. I hate myself for what I did to you. I took your love and trampled on it; I am so sorry I defiled you. As if that wasn't bad enough, I killed my own baby. Our baby.' At this, he choked up, then spoke angrily. 'I will never forgive myself for that. Never.' He broke down and wept.

'I know I don't deserve your forgiveness, but I pray that, some day, God will comfort your heart in such a way that you will be able to forgive me.'

Seeing Huss break down had deeply touched Angie, but she was afraid of the tenderness she felt. Instead, she responded angrily. 'Well, don't hold your breath. I don't even want to see you again, let alone forgive you.'

Huss looked at Angie in a way that made her feel confused, and caused her to look nervously down at the carpet. 'Angie, there is no pressure on you to see me. I will honour your decision but I want you to know that God loves you. You are a special person. One day, one day you will learn to love God. You see, every day since

I gave my life to God, I have prayed for you. I'm gonna go on praying until the day I die, that you will find peace, and freedom from the guilt that is destroying you. I love you, Angie.'

When Angie finally looked up, she was alone. Tears streamed down her face which she angrily brushed away.

16

Kenny walked down Manor Road between Stamford
Hill and Stoke Newington, towards the clothing business
his father owned and where he was learning the trade.
He was feeling quite cheerful, as Sunday had ended on a
positive note with Chrissy. Maybe he had over-reacted
about things, for his family weren't that orthodox and
surely would come around when they met her. Besides,
something about Chrissy almost looked Jewish. Maybe
somewhere in the past there was some Jewish blood; it
might be interesting to look into that. Anyway, this was
the twentieth century, and for goodness' sake, things
were not like they used to be. He closed his eyes and
imagined Chrissy smiling at him.

He was startled out of his musings when a car pulled
alongside him. The man in the back seat opened the
door and smiled. 'Excuse me, mate, do you know where
this is?' The man was pointing at a page in his A-to-Z.

As Kenny leaned over to help, he was suddenly
pushed from behind, into the car. His assailant quickly
climbed in behind, the car accelerating before the door
slammed shut.

'Hey! What's your game? Stop this car and let me
out.' Kenny reached for the door handle as the car
slowed down at a traffic light. He was immediately
punched hard in the ribs. Gasping in pain, he turned as

he heard a wicked-sounding snap as the man opened a flick-knife and held it against his ribs.

'Now shut up and sit still or I'm going to slash your face all over the shop.'

Terror gripped Kenny, and the muscles in his face began to twitch as he saw Stoke Newington Road flash by him in a blur. He tried to speak but could barely articulate. 'I've... I've only got twenty quid. You can have it, and my watch.'

The car pulled up a small side turning and came to a stop. One of the men roughly tied a black woollen scarf around Kenny's face to cover his eyes. Then, both men pushed Kenny into a prone position on the floor. Someone placed his foot on Kenny's face as the car began to accelerate. Within minutes, it was apparent they were going in circles around the back streets so Kenny would have no idea where they were going. Every so often the man's shoe would press harder against Kenny's face. Fighting nausea, his mind raced with thoughts of Chrissy, Nick, the restaurant, Sunday down by Tower Bridge; maybe they were kidnapping him, thinking he was somebody else. The car drew to a stop, an eerie silence surrounding him. The man with the foot in his face spoke to the other two.

'Listen, I'll go and get it all ready and you bring the Yid in.'

Kenny needed no more explanation. 'Bring the Yid in'; the words could have been spoken a thousand times down through history. As the two men roughly dragged him out of the car, his fear began to be replaced by hate. Why did he need to be protected? Where was Nick now anyway? Gritting his teeth, he decided he would not give them the satisfaction of weeping. Instead, this scum would have to work for it. The thought, strangely enough, made him feel good.

Kenny was taken into an empty warehouse and forced to sit on a wooden chair. Charlie Watson spoke. 'Now, you slimy little four-by-two. Nothing personal like, but you shouldn't be sniffing around girls from a superior race. Learn to stick to your own kind.'

Kenny spoke, 'Listen, Adolf, your breath stinks. You've been eating too much sauerkraut.'

Charlie picked up a brick and smashed it into Kenny's lower face. For a moment, everything went dark, then, in the darkness, there seemed to be a myriad of stars of various colours. As the shock began to wear off, pain hit him in waves, and he realised he was on the floor. Kenny ran his tongue over his mouth, then spat some broken teeth and blood out of his mouth.

Kenny sat up and with a twisted grin, asked sarcastically, 'What's wrong, Adolf, don't you like the truth? Why don't you just kill me?'

At this, Kenny's defenceless body was kicked. Syd then took a large spanner from a bag, and as Charlie and Fred held Kenny down, he smashed the spanner at Kenny's left kneecap. Kenny lay moaning, covered in blood, and fighting unconsciousness.

Charlie, leering with hate, leaned over his body. 'Now, this is just the beginning,' he hissed. 'If you squeal, you're a dead man, slowly. Keep away from little English black-eyed beauties, if you want to live.'

Kenny, fighting to maintain consciousness, knowing he had to say something, suddenly remembered and laughed hysterically. Then he shouted, 'I'm English, Adolf! I'm English! It may be your flag, but it's my country!'

The response was predictable. When they had vented their anger, three men dragged the unconscious form back into the car. When the darkness had receded sufficiently for Kenny to feel the intensity of the pain and be aware of his surroundings, he realised that he had been thrown out onto a country lane. Realising that they were gone, he began to moan, and to whisper Chrissy's name.

17

Rick ran up the steps to Huss's flat and knocked loudly on the door. When no one answered, he pounded insistently.

Slowly the door swung open, and Rick pushed inside. 'Hey man, what are you doing? Look, I don't feel in the mood to talk. Just leave me alone.'

Rick frowned as he spoke. 'I'm sorry, Huss, but it's Kenny. He's been done up by some mob. Broken bones, the whole works. They dumped him up at Enfield. I was going to take Chrissy, Nick, and Roulla to the hospital. I'm worried about Nick. Huss, he listens to you. You need to come because Nick might lose his marbles and go out and do something a bit wild.'

Chrissy, Nick, and Roulla sat in the back seat. Chrissy was slumped over in Roulla's arms, weeping. Rick and Huss sat in the front of the car. Nick sat absolutely silent chewing gum. He had a look on his face that none of his new friends had seen before.

Huss turned and looked at Nick. 'What's going on inside your head, man?'

Nick did not look at Huss but just kept on chewing. 'Nothing, man. I'm just upset about Kenny, like.' His voice sounded cold, detached, with an almost sinister quality about it.

Chrissy had stopped crying but was still enfolded by

Roulla's arms. Roulla's insides were in a state of chaos, partly because of Kenny and Chrissy, and partly because of seeing Nick act so strange. She thought that, somehow, Nick looked like 'Dirty Harry' or somebody like that.

They found the hospital and made their way to the ward where Kenny was. Chrissy leaned on Roulla for support as they entered the ward. There was nobody at Kenny's bed, as his family and rabbi had only recently left. The group came quietly in and sat around his bed. Chrissy took his one hand and kissed it, then began to cry as she held it to her face.

Kenny spoke, 'I've been thinking about you all—all day.' He tried to turn his head toward Chrissy but couldn't, so gently squeezed her hand.

'You are all so beautiful.' There was a softness in his voice. He had been given quite large doses of pain-killers and also tranquillisers.

Roulla reached out and held both Kenny and Chrissy's hands. 'We all love you, babe.'

Nick stood close to the bed and then spoke. 'Have the old Bill been to see you yet?'

Kenny replied, 'Where were you, man? I thought you were my resident head-cracker, always prepared for such situations.'

Nick didn't smile. 'Did the old Bill say who they thought it was?'

Kenny whispered, 'No idea. No one knows. Listen, everyone, can I just tell Nick something alone?'

Everyone stood up and walked to the end of the ward. Kenny reached out and held Nick's hand.

'Chrissy mustn't know this but I think your dad had some of his mates do this.'

Nick replied, 'I know, I felt it in my guts this morning.'

Kenny squeezed his hand tighter. 'What can we do? I

79

love her and I think in time, she will come to love me. What can we do?'

Nick tried to appear calm, looked at his watch and then spoke, 'Let's think about it—but you two just continue to take it a step at a time.'

Nick signalled to the others to return and then looked at his watch. 'I've got to use the bog.'

Chrissy reached out and held Kenny's hand again. 'What do the doctors say? Are you going to be all right?'

Kenny began to give a list of his wounds. They had not in fact broken his kneecap but had instead fractured his leg just beneath the kneecap. He had several fractured ribs, a concussion, and multiple cuts and bruises.

Meanwhile, Nick scribbled a note, then gave it to a nurse with the instruction to give it to Kenny. Walking outside, he took a minicab back to London.

About forty-five minutes later, the telephone rang in the Star and Garter pub. The barman was feeling harassed, as somehow some Celtic fans had made their way east and ended up in his pub.

'Look, this here's no reception centre and I'm not Harry Thompson's secretary, all right? Yeah, I've got it. Harry, go home quickly because someone in the family is sick. I said, I got it! All right? I got it.'

Nick waited in the phone box opposite the pub for his father to leave. As his car drove off, he made his way across the street. He was wearing a pair of rolled up levis and long black workman's boots. In his hand was a solid black baseball bat he had used in gang fights prior to becoming a believer. He made his way through the saloon bar, around the back to the private room. With one swift kick, the door burst off of its hinges, he then walked over the door now lying on the floor. His father's four friends rose simultaneously to their feet in a state of unexpected shock, as he stood coldly eyeballing them. Just as suddenly, Nick raised the baseball bat and smashed all the glasses and bottles that were on the table. The four men remained rooted to the spot.

'O.K., you lousy cowards. You've been polluting the atmosphere too long.' Turning to Charlie Watson, he snarled, 'You missed on this one. You're a loser, and now you're going to see more broken bones than you've had hot dinners.'

Nick's eyes flashed around the group, each trembling like a leaf, from fear. 'Two of you are going to die, the other two are going to be in hospital beds for a long time.'

Nick raised the bat into the air, high above his head, then brought it down with such force, that it smashed their drinking table in two.

Charlie Watson knew the expression of death when he saw it. 'Listen, son. Maybe we can talk about it.'

'Talk?' Nick exploded with rage, as he smashed a chair into pieces.

Charlie lost his nerve and in a whining voice began to plead. 'All right, all right, what do you want?'

Nick's face, contorted with hate, became even more intense. 'I want scum like you laying face down on the pavement, with your priest reading prayers over you.'

One of the other men completely lost his nerve. 'O.K.! O.K.! Anything! Anything, name it!'

Nick picked up his bat. 'All right, you burnt-out, pseudo-macho scum. Get your trousers, your shoes, and your socks off, and make it fast. Then you are going to take a walk down to the Bethnal Green nick. Once there you will report a crime—the beating of Kenny Levinson. If you don't, I assure you that bits and pieces of you will be scattered all over East London.'

Back at the hospital, a nurse walked down the ward and handed the piece of paper to Kenny, who was unable to focus on the words. 'What does this say, Chrissy?'

'It's from Nick!' Chrissy frowned as she read, 'Sorry,

81

man, but I'm late for a game of poker. Sometimes a bluff wins, but sometimes it loses. Whichever way, I want you to know that you are in my heart.'

On the reverse side was a note for Roulla, 'I'm sorry. Forgive me. I love you.'

Huss looked at the others and then threw his hands up in the air. Chrissy put her head down onto the bed moaning, 'Oh, no. Oh, no,' over and over. Roulla looked in dismay at everyone's reactions, and feeling a sense of unease, asked, 'What does it mean? What does it mean?'

Kenny tried to move his head again, but couldn't. Lifting his eyebrows, he murmured, 'You don't want to know.'

The Celtic fans had left without doing any damage to the pub and the landlord was in a good mood. Nick approached him, still holding the bat, to say there had been a bit of bother out back and he would pay for it. When the landlord saw the mess, he became angry.

Realising that Nick wanted to pay the damages, he calmed down. 'What can I say? Ying and Yang and all that. I got blessed by that Glasgow mob getting on their bikes before turning my Public Bar into a Swedish match-stick factory, and then I get cursed with a broken door, table and a fist-full of glasses. I'll have an estimate tomorrow. Pay it straight away and we'll leave it at that. Anyway, I don't want the old Bill sniffing around here.'

Nick walked out into the street, and over to the brick wall where he smashed the baseball bat in half, then slumped forward and began to cry.

Down the road, at the Bethnal Green Police Station, the staff sergeant was taking details for one of the most unusual arrests he had seen in over twenty-five years on the force. A female officer was typing, but finally unable to contain herself ran laughing into the other room. The following day the Hackney Gazette's headline story, 'Mysterious Lone Ranger Scares Pants off Local Mobsters!', complete with photos, hit the London streets.

18

Angie and Sheila sat together, talking about the way things had gone over the past six months. While they chatted, Rick rang from the hospital to tell Sheila that Kenny would be all right but he would be in hospital for some time. He then mentioned that Nick had gone off, and they were worried about him.

Sheila, greatly relieved about Kenny, but apprehensive about Nick who was a new believer, and prone to anger, told Angie what was happening.

Angie frowned. 'You're so different. It's kinda nice, you seem peaceful, and all, but you do go on about Jesus. It's kinda weird.'

'You know?' Sheila laughed. 'I'm glad you see a change in me. Sometimes I wonder about myself when I feel impatient or angry.' Sheila took a deep breath, 'Angie, Jesus is the most important person to me, in the whole world. There is nothing that can compare to his love.'

'You mean you love him more than Rick? That's unreal. I mean, Rick you can see and touch. But God is so far away. How can you compare the two? And besides, isn't Rick jealous?'

'No, he's not jealous. He is actually glad, because he knows that I can only love him properly, when I love God the most.'

'Oh, Sheila, you're unreal. Get with it. This is the twentieth century. Nobody talks about loving God. Not unless, maybe you're a nun.' Angie laughed cynically. 'Somehow, I just can't picture you in that role!'

Sheila broke into peals of laughter. 'Neither can I!'

'Fine. Now we've established that you're feeding me a line. So let's be honest. What is really going on inside of you? How come you don't hate me? In fact, if anything, you are nicer to me now than ever before. What gives?'

Sheila sat silent for a moment, as though lost in thought. Then she began to speak softly. 'I always felt so lost, 'cause my mum and dad died when I was just a kid. Well, as I grew older, I felt that somehow it was my fault. That if I had been good enough, you know, done things better, then my parents wouldn't have died. I missed them so much. At first, I could barely function. The pain was so overwhelming that in the end, I just felt that I had to escape from it.' Tears silently streamed down Sheila's face.

'Well, I laughed louder than anyone else, and I got up to all sorts of pranks as well. It was like I had to convince myself that I was having fun, then I wouldn't have to face the fear and the pain that threatened to destroy me. But the more I ran from my fears, the emptier I felt. You know, like there was a hole inside of me just eating me away. It was horrible.'

Angie shook her head in bewilderment. 'I never knew you felt like that. There were times I resented your carefree attitudes about everything.'

'Well, it was all just a cover-up. That day you walked away from me, I was devastated. I felt guilty, that I had failed you. Hating myself, I walked through the rain, longing to be able to do something to encourage you.'

Angie sat silent, the tears running down her cheeks, amazed that Sheila had cared so much, even then.

Sheila smiled wryly. 'Well, it was kinda strange because I suddenly found myself praying. You see, I couldn't understand how God could let such things happen. I told him that he was cruel and unfair, and then, suddenly, I found myself asking how I could find him, and pleading for his help. Can you imagine me, the one who never took anything seriously, actually asking God for help?

'Within moments, I heard music coming from an old wooden mission hall. Against my will, I was drawn towards the open door. Inside, a black man was singing about being lost and having no hope. I slipped quietly into a seat in the back, feeling quite self-conscious. When I got courage to look around, I saw a number of other young people there, so I didn't feel so out of place.

'Anyway, this bloke got up and started to talk about how we were all sinners but that God loved us anyway. Hearing his words cut like a knife through the mask I had put up, as I was confronted with the emptiness of my life. When he asked people to come forward to give their life to Christ, I found myself on my feet almost running down the aisle.'

Tears streamed silently down Sheila's cheeks as, smiling, she shook her head in wonder. 'God actually wanted me. All my life, I had been searching for someone to love me. Well, I found that need met in Jesus. That's why he is so important to me. You see, he filled that hole, and made me complete. I love him.'

Sheila looked deeply into Angie's eyes. 'You know, Angie, you're a bit like me. You're afraid, so afraid that you don't know what to do. You also feel guilty, just like I did. But you know, Angie, God loves you. He hurts when he sees you all torn up inside. He longs to fill your life with himself.'

Angie, weeping, shook her head angrily. 'No. He doesn't love me. How could he love someone like me? It's too late for me, Sheila. I'm just a worthless bit of trash! He could never love me!'

'Oh no, babe! That's not true. He loved you so much

that he died on the Cross for you, and as his blood was spilt, the penalty for your sins was paid. You see, he knew you couldn't handle it on your own, so he died in your place, so you could be set free from all that rubbish you're carrying. You're not trash! You're a china vase. Did you ever see a china vase thrown away because the flowers in it were dead? Of course not!'

Angie's eyes were filled with disbelief. 'Are you saying that I am valuable, but that the things inside me are what is bad?'

'That's exactly what I'm saying! God loves us, but hates our sin. The Bible teaches us that God must judge sin because he is holy. That is why Jesus had to die. He never sinned. He was like . . . like a lamb sacrificed on the altar to remove the penalty of our sins. It was his blood that was spilt, that washes us clean. It's his blood that empties out all the dead flowers.'

'Would he do it for me?'

'Oh Angie! He's here, waiting right this minute to do just that. Do you want to talk to him?'

Angie was sobbing as she nodded her head. Sheila prayed quietly, asking the Lord Jesus to help Angie give her life to him, and to fill her with his peace.

Then, very timidly, Angie began to pray. 'O Lord, I've really messed things up. I'm so sorry. Please help me. I need you to clean me like Sheila says. Oh, God. Help me!' A floodgate of tears seemed to be unleashed as Angie collapsed into Sheila's arms. The tears acted like a healing flow, washing out the oceans of pain that she had been bearing.

When her sobbing subsided, there was a sound of a blackbird in the tree outside their window.

'Angie, listen! Can you hear that sound? That bird is singing for you, to say there is a brand new day beginning, just for you.'

Angie looked through her tears out of the window.

Peace was reflected in her face, as she turned and smiled at Sheila. 'Oh Sheila. God really loves me, doesn't he?'
'Yes, Angie. He really does.'

19

Roulla turned the corner and through the gate into New-ington Green. She could see Nick sitting on a park bench, his Bible beside him, with his head in his hands, completely unaware of anything around him. She walked quietly up to him and placed a hand on his shoulder. He looked tired and haggard, his eyes were bloodshot, and he had a day's growth of beard.

He looked startled. 'How did you know I would be here?'

Roulla, her face expressing concern, shrugged her shoulders. 'I just knew.'

Sitting down beside him, she continued, 'Chrissy just rang and told me what happened. Your dad and a bloke called Jim are being questioned but not being charged with the rest of them.'

Nick shook his head back and forth. 'I failed. I failed Jesus, and I failed you. I let everyone down. I lied, I cheated, and, if that wasn't bad enough, I demolished half a pub.'

Roulla reached over and put her hand on his. 'Every-one has forgiven you. We were all a bit shocked but we realised what you were trying to do. I'm proud of you.'

He looked up at her, then shook his head in disgust. 'How can you say that? You don't want to hang around with a stick of dynamite.'

Squeezing his hand, she replied, 'You're wrong. I love you and want to spend the rest of my life with you. Hopefully, as time goes on, your method of dealing with problems will change. But look at you, Nick. You're not a hard nut bother boy anymore. You're becoming like a marshmallow. Why, I'll bet you cried straight after you went bananas.'

Nick looked up. 'How did you know?'

Roulla whispered, 'Because I know you.'

Feeling accepted and that there was hope for him, Nick threw back his head and laughed, then, quickly sobering, he looked out across Newington Green. 'How's Kenny? What is he saying?'

Roulla sat back and looked into the sky. 'It's funny, but he says he is looking forward to coming again on Tuesday night. He is also worried about you. He thinks that one day he is going to get you killed.'

Nick nodded. 'He's probably right.'

Roulla laughed. 'The big thing is that while we were at the hospital, Sheila helped Angie find Jesus!'

Nick stood up and then sat down. 'That's beautiful! What is Huss saying?'

Roulla laughed again. 'You know what Huss is like— the real cool one amongst us all? Well, Rick went to call Sheila while we were still at the hospital, and she told him about Angie. When Huss heard, he went absolutely out of his head, and shouted "Hallelujah!" at the top of his voice. Then he started hopping about, like he was doing some Red Indian dance. I didn't know Turks did that. Well, all the Enfield patients didn't know what to do. It was like they were trying to pretend he wasn't there. Anyway, here is spiritual Mr Wisdom, hotshot Christian being told off by the nurses for causing a disturbance!'

By now Nick was rolling around laughing. 'I can just see it! I can just see it!'

A little boy ran across the green, chasing a football.

The morning sun shone through the trees reflecting light in different directions as a gentle breeze ruffled the tired greenery in the midst of the city. Nick looked at Roulla. 'Will you marry me?'

Roulla's eyes lit up, sparkling like stars. She didn't speak but just nodded her head, a contented smile on her lips.

20

Chrissy and Nick sat in the kitchen, drinking coffee. The sun was actually shining again today, filling the room with a special atmosphere, especially appropriate for Saturday morning. The whole idea of being off work, lying in late, then being able to laze around doing whatever one fancied, was delightful. Chrissy was barefoot, wearing a pink track suit and sitting cross-legged on her chair. Nick, unshaven, was also barefoot, wearing a T-shirt and a pair of shorts.

Chrissy sipped her coffee and then spoke. 'It's funny, Nick, but have you noticed how everything has become so serious recently?'

Nick raised his eyebrows. 'That's the year's understatement.'

Chrissy cocked her head, frowning as she looked at her brother, 'Would you really have knuckled Dad's mates if they hadn't co-operated? I mean, really gone through with it?'

Nick looked down at his coffee cup, then began running his finger around the lip of the cup. He sighed deeply, then spoke sadly, 'It's hard to really know. I went there determined not to lose, but I did have the idea that I wanted them to hand themselves in. The problem would have been, if they tried to have a go at me. I was so angry that I think I might have cracked their heads open.'

Chrissy smiled. 'Maybe God protected you, or. . .' she laughed, 'maybe he protected them!'

Nick looked at his sister; how he loved her. 'That's an interesting thing for you to say. You know, about God.'

Chrissy smiled again. 'Well, Kenny and I have talked it over and we feel like we're not actually believers, but we're associates of your little Tuesday night mob.'

Nick joked, 'Maybe we could call ourselves the Church of the Tuesday Night Mob!'

Chrissy smiled, stood up, stretched, shook her hair and then sat down again. 'I love Roulla and Sheila, they're beautiful people. I feel clean and good when I am around them.'

She stood up again and walked nervously around the room. 'What would you think about me and Kenny getting married?'

Nick put his cup down. 'Isn't it a bit soon or sudden, I mean, well, you know. It might be, that seeing him all beat up got to you emotionally, and that you might not really love him.'

Chrissy looked straight into Nick's eyes, 'Actually, I've thought about that. But I really liked him right from the beginning. I guess, maybe though, what has happened might have speeded things up a bit. Besides, haven't things been moving along with you and Roulla?'

Nick laughed, 'Very observant, aren't you? Yes, I want to marry her. Though I think it will be harder for you two because of the family and everything.'

Chrissy sat down in her original yoga position. 'I know, but it's not going to be straightforward for you, either. Dad hates the Greeks and her family might like you as a friend, but they may not be so keen about you as a family member.'

Their conversation was interrupted as the phone rang.

'Hi, Nick, this is Huss. How are you doing on the TNT job?'

'Well, Huss, to be honest, I've been repenting about baseball bats more than anything else. But it's going great with Roulla. I just asked her to marry me yesterday. So now we have an understanding that we will only hold hands. I'm determined to do what we said.'

'That's great, Nick! We need to continue to pray for each other, that the Lord will help us remain pure in our minds.'

21

When Chrissy had told Nick she had decided to go to the Bible study, Nick had smiled and told her to be ready an hour early.

Meanwhile, Kenny lay looking at the ceiling. Knowing that no one planned to visit that night, he was feeling decidedly sorry for himself. To his astonishment, and pleasure, at 7.15 p.m., the entire Bible study group, along with Angie, paraded in and took up position around his bed.

'Hey! What's going on?'

Nick shrugged his shoulders, looking at the group, 'Come on, let's go. He doesn't want us here.'

'Of course I want you here. But what about your study? This is Tuesday, you know.'

'Hey. Listen to the man.' Nick laughed. 'Seriously, Kenny, we felt we just couldn't have a really good discussion without you, so...here we are. Do you think you can put up with us?'

Kenny laughed. 'I was just feeling sorry for myself, and you lot have made my day. Well, what's the topic of discussion tonight?'

'What's the difference between a Jew and a Christian?' Huss smiled. 'Anyone got any ideas?'

Nick looked up at the ceiling. 'I would say that they are the same, except the Jews don't believe in Jesus.'

Roulla chipped in. 'But Jesus was a Jew, so were all the early mob of his followers like Peter, John and Paul.'

Rick looked at Kenny, who paused, then spoke. 'Jesus. Definitely, he is the difference, but things are different, now. Then there was no religion, now there is. Knowing Jesus then, was all wrapped up in loving each other and loving God. Now it's not like that. Christians and Jews have got two thousand years of hostile actions against each other.'

'Kenny is right about that. There has been a lot of injustice that has gone on, down through history. But what if we could keep our traditions and rituals but still go back to the original ideas that Jesus had?' asked Huss.

Kenny laughed. 'I feel like I am being set up.'

'But you know us. You could hardly call us religious.'

Kenny replied. 'You keep saying that but you are already beginning to develop your own rituals and culture. Even though you go to church on Sunday, your big thing is Tuesday night. You, Huss, are like the rabbi or the priest. You use a lot of your own style of talking, like, "We're believers," or, "Jesus is in my heart." Do you know what I mean?'

Huss paused. 'You're right, but I don't think we're an institution. Really, if you think about it, you don't have to be anything or do anything to be a part of us. Like we love you and feel you are as much a part of us as anybody else.'

Kenny responded, 'But there is a difference, and it is Jesus. I think if I'm honest, I want you all to be my friends, but leave it as it is concerning our beliefs and stuff.'

Chrissy shocked everybody by saying, 'Listen, couldn't we somehow be both, you know, be believers but be Jewish?'

Kenny was stunned. 'But you were the one who said you weren't anything at all.'

Chrissy began to choke up. 'I know, but when I saw

you all smashed up and laying in that bed, I realised that life was different than I thought. I was scared. I realised that I do need God.'

At that point, the ward sister came in to say that visiting hours were over. Huss smiled at her. 'Could we just have a couple of minutes to pray for Kenny?'

Raising her eyebrows, she responded, 'You're the Red Indian dancer, aren't you? Make sure it's a short prayer—and quiet!'

As everyone bowed their heads, Kenny coughed nervously. 'Lord,' Huss prayed, 'we want to thank you for your love. In this world, of so much hatred and turmoil, we need you, to give meaning to our lives. Lord, we pray for Kenny, that you would heal his body. Thank you for sparing his life. Please bless him with your love in such a special way, that he knows it is you, and that he may come to know you as his dearest friend. Amen.'

Angie had come along with Rick and Sheila. Feeling very shy, and somewhat nervous about being around Huss, she had just sat quietly listening to the others. As the group left the hospital, Huss went over to Angie. When she realised that he meant to speak to her, she immediately looked away from him. 'Angie, I'm really happy for you. Rick told me you've become a believer. There will be days when things are hard for you. Remember then that God loves you, just as you are.'

'Hmph! I don't remember asking for your advice!' Angie responded sharply, then quickly moved forward between Sheila and Chrissy.

22

In the following weeks, time passed quickly for Angie, as she read her Bible and talked with Sheila about what she had read. One Friday evening Sheila approached her. 'Angie, I need to talk to you.'

Looking up from her Bible, Angie smiled. 'Yes?'

Sitting beside her, Sheila nervously twisted her hanky. 'Angie, Huss normally comes over on Saturday, to work out what will be covered on Tuesday evening. I was wondering if, well, now that you've been a believer for some time, if you would mind him coming?'

Angie looked shaken. 'I didn't realise. I, ahh, well, maybe I could just go out somewhere before he comes.'

'Oh no. We don't want you to feel nervous; after all, this is your home. I know you have every right to hate Huss for what he did to you. It was wrong and it was right to be angry about it for a time.' Bowing her head, she spoke hesitantly, 'But God wants us to give our anger to him. Did you know that Jesus teaches us to forgive our enemies? Those who have hurt us?'

Angie's eyes widened in disbelief. 'You expect me to forgive that, that...?'

'I don't, because I know it isn't something that comes easy. I have struggled with something similar for months.'

Angie lashed out in anger. 'What have you struggled

98

with that can even be compared to being raped?

Sheila got up and walked over to the window. After a few moments, she began to speak brokenly. 'I do know something of what you are experiencing. I know the pain, the fear, the shame, the guilt...' A sob was wrenched from deep inside her.

Angie looked shocked at the horror she saw on her friend's face, as Sheila turned towards her. 'Sheila! What is wrong?'

Tears streamed down Sheila's face, and holding out her hands as if asking for mercy, she spoke. 'It was my grandad. I went to live there when my parents died. At first, he would just touch me, and tell me that I mustn't tell anyone, or I would die too. Then he began to rape me. That went on for several years, until I was ten. I ran away and that was when they put me in a foster home.'

'I didn't know, Sheila.'

'No one knew. It was so horrible that I totally blocked it out of my mind. When I became a believer, God brought it back into my memory so that I could deal with it. There have been moments that I have been caught in the grips of terror, lest somehow it happen again. What helped me was taking the verse, "God has not given us a spirit of fear, but of power, of love, and of a sound mind," as my very own. Every time I was afraid, I would thank Jesus that he was with me. But I really hated my grandfather. I also hated any man involved in child abuse or rape. When God asked me to forgive him, I was angry, just like you. I told God, my grandfather did not deserve to be forgiven, and that I would hate the man until I died. But God has gently been persisting with me and because I wanted to please him more than hang on to my right to hate, I asked him to help me. It hasn't been easy, but the exciting thing is that once I let go of my hatred, my grandfather no longer had power to hurt me. I am learning to forgive others too; I know because I did not hate Huss when he told us what he had done.

Instead, I felt compassion for his grief. Angie, God forgave us, and now he asks us to be like him and to forgive others.'

Angie jumped up in horror. 'Are you serious? Do you really mean to tell me that I have to forgive him?' Tears running down her cheeks, she added cynically, 'What happens if I don't? Does God stop loving me?'

Sheila quickly went to Angie and put her arms around her. 'Oh, Angie. Of course not. Nothing we do can ever stop God from loving us. I know what I am saying seems harsh and unfair to you. But you see, your anger can only hurt yourself. It can't undo what happened to you.'

Angie began trembling with fear, as the memory of her rape seemed to engulf her. Sobbing she cried, 'I hate him! I hate him! And I will never, never forgive him!'

Running to her room, she locked the door, and threw herself on the bed, where she spent the night weeping into her pillow. About four o'clock in the morning, she got up and, putting the light on, opened her Bible. Her eyes fell on the words, 'Whatever you did for one of the least of these brothers of mine, you did for me.' The tears began to fall again, only this time there was a calmness.

'Lord, I don't want to forgive Huss. I hate him for what he did to me, for what I have become. You ask me to forgive him. I can't. But maybe you can forgive him for me. O Lord. I want to please you. Please help me.'

A feeling of peace enfolded her, and, to her amazement, she found herself humming a tune she had heard Sheila singing. Lying back on her pillow, cradling her Bible in her arms, within seconds she fell into a deep, restful sleep.

Waking around noon, she found herself smiling and humming. Then, remembering, she jumped out of bed. Quickly she dressed and went out to the kitchen where she found Rick and Sheila enjoying a late cup of coffee.

Giggling as she entered the room, Rick and Sheila looked up in amazement.

'Guess what? God really does live in my heart!'

'Of course he does, Angie.' Sheila frowned with concern.

Giggling again, Angie went on, 'No. I mean, he really lives in my heart. Remember you said that I would know he lived inside of me, when he began changing my attitudes, and all? Well, last night I was angry with you for telling me I needed to forgive Huss. I cried most of the night.'

'We know. We spent most of the night praying for you, that God would help you in your pain.'

'You were praying for me?' Angie asked, astonished when they both nodded their heads. 'Well, he answered your prayers. He comforted me, and he is changing my attitude towards Huss. I told God, I was willing for him to help me forgive Huss. I don't know if I have or not, but all the anger seems to be gone!'

Sheila jumped up and ran over to Angie. 'Oh Angie, I'm so glad.' The two girls hugged, both weeping for joy.

An hour later, Rick went downstairs to wait for Huss. When he arrived, Rick smiled. 'Hey man! God is wonderful!'

Huss smiled. 'What's going on? I thought this place was off-limits for me?'

'That's just it. Sheila told Angie she needed to forgive you. It nearly blew her mind, but she's a real trooper. She was up all night and in the end, told God she was willing to forgive you.'

'Come again?'

'She isn't bitter anymore. It's like she's a different person.'

Huss's eyes welled with tears.

'Now don't expect too much. Just take it real slow and easy. If you give her enough space, I know God will bring you two together.'

With deep joy, the two began to pray, expressing their gratitude for the wonder of what they were watching God do in Angie's life.

23

The house was still quiet as Nick rolled over in bed and stretched. Yawning, he decided to get up and read his Bible. Twenty minutes later, deep in study, he suddenly jumped up, smashing his fist into his hand. 'Blast!' Looking angry, he stamped out of his room and down the stairs to the phone, and picked up the receiver.

'Hey man, what's going on?' Huss asked, surprised to be called so early in the morning.

Nick exploded, 'It just doesn't work! Maybe it does for you, but it doesn't for me.'

'What are you talking about?'

'Our TNT pact. I just can't keep my mind pure. I feel so dirty. I mean, how can I think such thoughts when I'm reading my Bible? God must really be disgusted with me.' Sneering, he spoke sarcastically. 'It's all right for people like you. You never seem to struggle like I do.'

Huss bowed his head, and spoke softly. 'I've really been going through it, seeing Angie and all. It's like she's so close but yet so distant. These last few days have been hell. I constantly struggle with guilt and shame. No. It's not easy for me.'

'Hey, man, I didn't know. I thought you had it made. Like you're so much more spiritual than me.'

A wry smile creased Huss's face. 'Hold on, let me get my Bible. Maybe we can find something to help us both.'

Picking up his Bible, he looked in the back, then flipping the pages, began to read from the first Letter of John. 'It says here that if we confess our sins, God will forgive us.'

'Yeah, but how many times? Surely he doesn't want us to keep coming back over and over again for the same thing. There has to be a limit. I mean, otherwise God will think we're messing him about.'

'But Nick, didn't Jesus tell his disciples that they have to forgive seven times seventy? If God expects us to forgive that many times, surely he will forgive us more than that. And maybe God doesn't keep count like we do.' Huss continued searching in his Bible. 'Hey! Listen to this! It says in Isaiah that he has swept away our sins, and that they are gone like the morning mist at noon.'

Nick, who was now looking in his Bible, said, 'Man! Listen to this verse. "I, even I, am he who blots out your transgressions for my own sake, and remembers your sins no more." If God doesn't remember our sins, then you must be right, he doesn't keep count. So each time I sin, it is the first time to him. So that means he isn't angry with me.'

Huss nodded his head, a look of joy on his face. 'That means we don't need to feel guilty. All we need to do is confess our sin, and he instantly washes us clean. I think you and I need to talk to the Lord right now!'

After praying, both encouraged, they chatted for a while. Then Huss spoke.

'I was thinking that maybe we could have a "welcome home" party for Kenny, when he gets out from his middle class porridge. A dinner party with all the gang would be nice.'

The two friends spoke for several minutes and then hung up. Nick called upstairs to Chrissy to turn the music down. Then going to turn off the kettle, whose whistle sounded like a siren, he realised how thrilled he was to be alive.

As Nick turned to get the milk, he nearly collided with

his father. Harry Thompson's face was filled with bitterness. 'Do you know what they got today in court?'

Nick spoke firmly, but without hatred. 'Not half of what I would have given to them if they hadn't handed themselves in.'

'You really think you're a hotshot, don't you? Because you're young and strong, you think you can pick on older blokes. Well, they got three years probation and three years suspended sentence, on condition they don't contact Chrissy or your Jew bag. You give us all this religious stuff, then you go around lying and threatening people.'

'Listen, Dad, this is really hard for me because, believe it or not, I love you. But your little has-been mobsters took a mate of mine and nearly killed him. They messed up his face, so that he's got to have false teeth. He will probably walk with a limp for the rest of his life. And you want me to be sorry for your friends?'

Harry wanted to hit Nick but realised that those days were over. He didn't like Nick's religion anyway. It smacked of anarchy and Communist agitation. Discipline was the only answer for these kids today, he thought to himself. 'Well, get this. You and your sister are no longer welcomed here, so get your stuff and get out. Go move in with one of those Jewish families. They've all got AIDS anyway.'

Nick threw his hands up in despair. 'All right. I can't stand all the hassle between us. The break may do everybody some good.'

Harry turned away. 'You can come back any time you're willing to admit the Yids are scum and that we'd best keep away from them.'

24

Huss wore his blue three-piece suit and white shirt. With his new haircut, he looked utterly respectable. Now walking nervously down the street towards Angie's parents, he thought it would have been easier phoning to apologise, but then decided it was more in order, much as he dreaded it, to go in person. Standing in front of the door, he apprehensively ran his finger between his collar and his neck. Summoning up the courage, he rang the bell.

Mr Greenaway, who answered the door, was nearly six feet, and weighed sixteen stone. His arm, as thick as most people's necks, flashed forward, as his fist shot into the centre of Huss's face. Huss fell back onto the pavement. Dazed, he looked down at his new suit, now covered with blood. Unable to breathe through his nose, he gingerly touched it, finding it a different shape than normal. Just as suddenly, Mr Greenaway lifted Huss off the ground, and head butted his face. Stars filled Huss's vision, as he felt himself being whirled around. Then, lifting him from behind, Mr Greenaway literally tossed Huss into the street.

Waving his fist angrily, he shouted, 'If you ever show your greasy face around here again, then your family will have to peel you off twenty kebab skewers. Got it?'

In the distance, Huss heard the door slam shut. Sitting

in a crumpled heap in the street, waves of pain hit him.
He reeled and fell as he tried to stand up. He groaned,
feeling like dozens of hammers were hitting him in the
head, and a knife-like pain was travelling up his back.
Slowly and painstakingly he got on all fours. Then, holding onto the three-foot garden wall, he pulled himself
up. His head still spinning, he stumbled up the path to
the door. 'Well, Jesus. Here we go again.' Pressing the
doorbell, he cautiously stepped back.

Mr Greenaway, opening the door, could hardly
believe his eyes. 'Have you gone off your rocker?'

As he moved forward, Huss raised his hands in front
of his face. 'Wait! Mr Greenaway, give me a break. I've
got to talk to you about Angie.'

A woman about five feet tall appeared in the doorway, wearing an apron over her dress, and holding a
wooden spoon in her hand. Seeing Huss, she shrieked,
'My God, Bill! What in heaven's name is happening?
Did you do this to the poor boy?'

Mr Greenaway began to sputter, 'Poor boy? Why,
this dirty Mediterranean greaseball...'

Mrs Greenaway pushed him aside. 'You clumsy
brute.'

Putting her arm around Huss, she helped him into the
house. 'Come in here, you poor thing. Don't take any
notice of this brute, he's all mouth and no action.' Huss,
who felt like a battered punching bag, found it hard to
agree with her.

Taking him into the kitchen, she began to gently wash
all his wounds. As she worked, she spoke. 'I saw Angie
yesterday. She's a changed girl. She told me all about
trying to kill herself, then going to Sheila's and how
Sheila took her in.' Mrs Greenaway took out her hanky
and dabbed at her eyes. 'She was a good girl, she was.
Why did you go and hurt her? She trusted you. Whenever her dad would warn her about you, she would just

smile and say, "If you knew Huss, you wouldn't worry. He's not like that." '

Huss lowered his head in shame. 'I'm sorry. I feel so ashamed that I used your daughter, and then tossed her aside. She was afraid of her dad finding out that she was pregnant. I used that to make her have an abortion. It was the easiest for me, you see. Since I became a believer in Jesus, I have hated myself for what I did. That's why I came here today. To ask you and Mr Greenaway to forgive me.

'You know, I deserved the beating your husband gave me. In a strange way, I am glad he did it. Somehow, it makes me feel better.' Tears filled Huss's eyes. 'Mrs Greenaway, I do love your daughter. She doesn't know I am here, but I am hoping that one day she will marry me.'

'Angie told me you had got religious. I believe in that stuff, it makes people gentle.' Turning, she yelled, 'Bill, get out here!' Bill Greenaway walked timidly into the kitchen. Angie's mum suddenly picked up the newspaper and hit him on the head. 'Look what you've gone and done to his suit! Go and find him a hundred quid.'

Huss began to protest, 'No, really! That's O.K.' Mrs Greenaway stood with her hands on her hips, frowning at her husband. 'Please, it doesn't matter. Anyway, it only cost sixty-five quid. I mean, I don't want money, I just want to speak to you both. Please, Mr Greenaway, give me a chance to explain why I'm here.'

That evening when Huss walked into the sitting-room at Rick and Sheila's, his face was swollen and had ripened into a series of blacks and blues. His nose had been straightened at the hospital, but looked worse than it was with an aluminium clip holding it in place. Angie, coming from the kitchen, started in horror when she saw him. 'Whatever have you been doing?'

Huss shrugged his shoulders. 'I just paid a visit to your parents.'

Angie's hands flew to her face, as she gasped, 'Did my father do that?'

Huss nodded his head.

Rick stood by laughing. 'Sorry, Huss. But you look like that evil geezer in Star Wars!'

Huss tried to smile, but it hurt. 'Your dad sure packs a powerful punch, but then your mother isn't half bad herself.'

'She hit you too?'

Huss made an attempt at a chuckle. 'She dropped a ton of bricks, but it wasn't on me. It was on your dad.'

Everyone laughed. Then, frowning, Angie asked, 'Why ever did you go to my home, anyway? You must have known my father wouldn't be too happy to see you.'

Huss looked a little embarrassed. 'I've been reading in the Old Testament about when you steal something, you gotta repay it. I didn't think it was for today, did I? Well, every time I tried to pray, it seemed that God kept hitting me over the head about going to your parents and telling them I was sorry for what I had done to you. I fought against it for a week—I mean, like, I really didn't want to see your dad. Last night, when I couldn't sleep, I told God I would try to make it right. So I went.'

Rick looked serious. 'You know, man, I really respect your courage. I know it wasn't an easy thing for you to do. But God will bless you for obeying him.'

Later that evening as Angie lay awake in her bed, she realised that seeing Huss all bashed up had really got to her. Learning that it was because he wanted to make things right with her parents, had touched her deeper than she wanted to admit. Frowning, she began to carry on a conversation with herself. 'Why did he do it? It was crazy. He had to know Dad would be furious. Could it be that he is really getting serious about life? About responsibility? That he might be trustworthy? Oh, I don't know. What if he isn't really different? But he did take a beating from Dad. The old Huss wouldn't have been caught dead visiting my parents. He must be different.'

Closing her eyes, she began to pray. 'Lord, I am so confused. It is exciting to think that Huss might really love me, but I feel so afraid. When I think of that horrible day, love seems so...well, horrible. I know I used to love him, but now? I just don't know. I need your help to put all the pieces of my life back together in some sort of order. Oh, how I wish I could be like Sheila. She doesn't worry like me, but is so relaxed, and so enjoys Rick. Oh Lord, please help me.'

25

Roulla walked up to her mother and father who were watching the television. Moving in front of the screen, she twirled around like a model on the stage. 'Yoohoo, can I get your attention, my maternal and paternal symbols of love and justice? This is your daughter.' She knelt down. 'The one whom the very character of our ancestors is embodied within.' She spread her arms as if she was giving a finale to a great opera. 'These genes and chromosomes in whom is engraved the anatomical essence of Alexander the Great, Zorba the Greek, Christina Onassis, and, may I add, Costas the kebab man on the corner of Chatham Avenue! In other words, can we turn the telly off? I need to talk to you.'

Roulla's father looked in awe at his daughter. Turning to his wife he said, 'It's like a machine. Tell me not. Like one of those clockwork monkeys you wind up and it chatters for thirty-eight seconds.'

Roulla walked to the couch on her knees, and reaching out, put her arms around both her parents. 'Oh, I love you, Mum and Dad. You have given me so much love. When I look around and see all the unhappy people in the world, I'm just so grateful that God gave me you as parents.' She sat back, still on her knees, and then moved into a cross-legged position. 'Look, Nick is coming around any minute now and we wanted to talk to you together.'

Roulla's mother raised her eyebrows. 'Androulla, is that why you were scurrying around tidying up? Why do you do this without telling me? I would have baked something.'

'Oh, Mum, it's O.K. Just sit back and relax. Be natural, spontaneous, your wonderful self!'

Androulla's father spoke. 'You really are wound up tonight. Maybe someone should answer the door, which happens to be ringing.'

Roulla rushed into the hall and opened the door. To say Nick looked nervous was an understatement. 'How do I look?' he whispered.

Roulla replied, 'Like a Greek.'

Nick walked into the room, did a perfect job on pronunciation, and told Roulla's mother that she looked younger than the last time he had seen her.

They chatted for a couple of minutes, when Roulla, her eyes sparkling, said, 'Mum and Dad, Nick has something to say.'

Nick, who had been hoping for two hours of small talk, nearly choked. He felt he should stand up for the occasion, but then thought that might not be appropriate. Every eye upon him, as they waited expectantly, he began coughing to give himself a moment's reprieve. Then, clearing his throat, he began, 'Mr and Mrs Kyriacou, Androulla and I have been special friends now for some time and, well, our hearts have become quite warm toward each other.' He wanted to start again, but for him to stop, say, 'Cut. Take two,' just wouldn't be understood. 'Well, when we started seeing each other, we made a pact that we wouldn't do anything together that we couldn't do in front of you.' He fidgeted in his chair as he thought of smashing the glasses and bottles in the Star and Garter pub. They probably wouldn't be too keen on him doing that in front of them, but he had said

112

together, and Roulla wasn't with him. He continued. 'I realise that Androulla is Greek, even though she was born here in London. I love Greek culture and have encouraged Androulla to be proud about being Greek.' Androulla picked the tuft of her hair that formerly had been orange and shook it.

'Also, I've tried to understand the problems of Cyprus, the 1974 invasion, Aeoka B. Grevus, Nikkos Sampsun, Makarios, and the whole Turkish-Greek situation.' Roulla looked at him in awe. He was incredible, she thought to herself.

'Today, I got Milovan Djilas's book about hiding in the Macedonian mountains during the Greek Civil War. Well, all this is to say that I love your daughter. By that, I mean that I care about her and want the best for her life. And I—ah—I was wondering if there was any way that you would consider me as a worthy candidate to be your daughter's husband.'

Roulla's mother and father looked at each other, then at Roulla, and then at Nick. Mr Kyriacou spoke. 'You girls go outside. I want to talk to Nick alone.' Roulla wasn't sure if this was a good sign or a bad one. They left by way of the kitchen door and began to put together some food and drinks.

Mr Kyriacou spoke sternly. 'Do you swear to me that you've not touched my daughter?'

Nick spoke earnestly. 'I swear to you. Also, we've never kissed. We've held hands and, when I was upset, she hugged me, but absolutely nothing else.'

'How about money? What have you got to offer her?'

Nick looked down at the carpet and then up at Roulla's father. 'I've just started training to be an engineer for British Telecom, and I really enjoy the work. At the moment, I have about four hundred quid in the building society, not much really. But I do have a heart that wants to give her the best. I don't smoke, drink, or gamble, so it's possible to save money.'

Mr Kyriacou sat back. 'I won't make a decision tonight, but we'll talk again next week. By the way, my cousin Stellios drinks at the Star and Garter. He's also a waiter at the Spartan, so he recognised you when you smashed up those neo-Nazi scum bags. That was a touch of class, Nick. I'm impressed.'

Nick's mouth dropped open in amazement. Just then the two women walked into the room with a tray of biscuits, cakes and tea, providing a welcome distraction.

Roulla blurted out, 'Well, what did you say, Dad?'

'I said we need to think about it. We can talk about it next week.'

Roulla thought she would explode. She looked at Nick, who gave her a look that said relax, don't rock the boat, the stakes are high. The subject of marriage was dropped, and Nick's educational programme began. He learned of the Greek migration to Cyprus over twelve hundred years ago, the Turkish usurping armies who had come only yesterday to the island, even though yesterday was four hundred years ago. As he absorbed the information with genuine interest, he realised how comfortable he was here with Roulla's parents and how he would not mind calling them Mother and Father.

26

Tonight, Chrissy had come on her own to the hospital, as she needed some time to talk to Kenny. His face was healing well and the doctors had decided to combine his dental work with what they were doing with the rest of his therapy. He looked one hundred per cent better than just ten days ago.

Chrissy began by telling Kenny that she had moved into Rick and Sheila's and was sleeping on the couch in the front room. Nick had moved into Huss's bedsit and was roughing it in a sleeping-bag on the floor. As she spoke, she realised that she really wanted to be with Kenny; there was no turning back.

Holding hands, they talked of their love and how special it was and how sometimes one connects so deeply with another that life without that person is just incomplete. Chrissy leaned forward and gave Kenny a light kiss on the cheek.

He smiled absent-mindedly, then spoke. 'You know, I've been thinking about the conversations we've had about Jews and Christians and Jesus.'

Chrissy interrupted. 'The way you answer the questions has a particular ring to it that I can't explain. It's as if there's more to you than appears on the surface. Like a missing piece of information that, if we had, we would understand where you're coming from. You become deeper and deeper the more I'm with you.'

Kenny looked at Chrissy with a probing stare. 'You're right. There is something more I haven't told you.'

Chrissy leaned forward and whispered, 'Can you share it with me now?'

Kenny smiled. 'Of course, but don't say anything to the others about it. O.K.?'

She nodded, and he began. 'Your brother, Nick, is really special to me. After the time on the underground when he saved me and started talking about Jesus, it really shook me up inside. I didn't realise how ignorant I was about Jesus and all. When I was about fifteen, a group of businessmen came to the school where I went. They gave everyone half a Bible, you know, the Christian half, the new bit. I just took it home, stuck it on the shelf and didn't think any more about it. Well, after that time with Nick, I decided to find out who this Jesus was that the Christians were talking about. So I started reading, actually studied really. The first section that just talked about Jesus blew my mind. I couldn't escape him. He was awesome. You know, all the stories and stuff, well, the Jesus that I found there I loved. I mean, honest, Chrissy, I can't explain it. I just loved him. Well, then I met you and I saw Nick again, and when I came round and your dad did his number like, well, you know, when Nick was so deeply upset outside in the street, it was like deep within me I realised that the Jesus I saw in the book was coming out of Nick's life and touching me and loving me.' He paused to reflect.

Chrissy said, 'That's beautiful, beautiful.'

'You see, I'm more sensitive than I look. Don't laugh, O.K.? But you remember I told you about those kids putting pig fat all over me? Well, they took my little Rupert Bear, and pulled his arms and legs off. Sometimes I still dream about my little bear, and then when I wake up, I feel the same pain of longing for him back again.'

Chrissy's eyes filled with tears. 'Oh, I'm so sorry.'

'Well, that night with you and Nick started to bring out all that sensitive side of me. I just wanted the Jesus I found in the book to be real, not a story, but real.' Kenny paused and then continued, 'Well, I went to see our rabbi to talk to him about it. He was pleased to see me because I really only go to synagogue when my grandmother hassles me, or like for Yom Kippur—you know, special times of the year. Well, I told him about what I was feeling about Jesus, and he was very understanding. He gave me a book to read by Dagobert Rune, one of our Jewish writers, giving the history of the Jews and the Christians down through the years.

'Well, unfortunately it's pretty bad stuff that went on. The early Christians were always writing against the Jews. This one guy, Chrysostom, taught that Jews were the enemies of God, so all Christians should hate them. In the Middle Ages, a bishop in France used to drag a Jew through the city every year; then in the market-place he'd slap him in the face, declaring that his fathers had killed Jesus.

'Then some heavyweight, I think it was Luther, said that the Jews must be herded like gypsies into barns. He said that their rabbis should be allowed to teach only under the threat of death. Hitler quoted all this stuff to justify gassing and burning six million men, women, and children.'

He sighed and looked at Chrissy. 'I would love to have Jesus, but I can't betray who I am and join myself to all this history.'

Chrissy looked at this young, complex man whom she loved so dearly. 'I just want what you want, Kenny.' Then putting her head in her hands, she moaned, 'O God, life is so complicated, so complicated.'

27

Nick and Roulla sat together in Newington Green. The tiny oasis in the midst of the concrete forest was to them a glimpse of Eden. Nick stood up and walked once around the bench that Roulla was sitting on. 'You know, I've been thinking a lot about when I went into the pub and stuff. Well, my immediate guilt was because I threatened those blokes and actually could have done them up. Also, I felt bad because of the damage I did. Well, this morning when I was reading the Bible . . . I'm doing three chapters a day; it's fabulous! It really gets your marbles going. Anyway, I read this stuff about obeying the authorities.'

He climbed onto the seat next to the one Roulla was sitting on and began to tightrope walk along the narrow top of the back rest. Roulla laughed and then spoke. 'You'd better watch it, or you'll be in bed next to Kenny.'

Nick jumped down and sat down next to the girl he loved. He leaned back linking his hands behind his head. 'Well, the thing is, I was doing a "Charles Bronson Death Wish job". You know, taking the law into my own hands. I think that that was as bad as smashing up the joint. Thing is, I've let them know that I would do it again. But truthfully, I don't think that I could because of what I read today.'

Roulla faced him. 'Are you going to tell them that?'

Nick looked at the grass. 'No, let them read the Book and find out for themselves. Till then, what they don't know won't hurt them.'

Roulla laughed. 'You're incredible, absolutely incredible!'

28

'Rick. Hey, this is Kenny, via the high tech communications of the Enfield Hospital telephone trolley, donated by the Rotary Club.'

Rick replied, 'Your voice does seem deeper than normal. It's amazing what modern science can produce.'

Kenny laughed. 'Rick, man, I need some help but it must be kept an absolute secret. I need you to go somewhere and do something for me.'

'Sure, but is it so secret that even I can't know about it?'

'Listen, you bozo, get a pen and paper and write this down.' Kenny gave a whole list of instructions to Rick who transcribed them carefully.

'I'm due for a day off, so I'll get on it, and then get back to you with it. How's the leg?'

'Yeah, great, but when I woke up yesterday, I found someone had written on the plaster, "Britain for the British!" '

Rick laughed. 'Yeah, I can understand that, what with the people you're hanging around with!'

As Rick hung up, he carefully put the paper into his pocket.

On the following Tuesday, Kenny was to be released from the hospital.

The group excitedly arranged for him to come around

to Rick and Sheila's for the Bible study, where they would then surprise him with a 'welcome home' party. Sheila and Angie had decorated the front room with streamers and 'welcome back' signs, and prepared a nice meal. Chrissy had baked a large cake, decorating it with a heart. Inside the heart was the star of David and inside of that was a cross. She had become excited at the idea and kept it to herself. Everyone was in the room except Rick, who had gone to pick up Kenny.

Once in the car, Rick handed Kenny a piece of paper. 'Here it is, but it took the entire day. I thought I was going to have to get a season-ticket for the place!'

As Kenny began to study the paper, he smiled to himself, folded the paper in half, and neatly put it in his pocket.

The car pulled up outside the flats, and Rick helped Kenny out of the car. With his cane, and Rick's help, he was able to slowly make his way up the stairs. Arriving at the door, Rick rang the bell rather than using the key. The door burst open and everyone began to cheer and clap. The following celebration for Kenny was one of the most beautiful experiences of his life. As he was escorted into the front room, he kept shouting, 'I feel loved, I feel loved!'

Then he saw the cake. He looked around and then looked at Chrissy. 'Did you...?' She nodded. He smiled. 'Lovely, absolutely lovely.'

The merriment continued for some time, until Kenny raised his hand into the air for silence. 'I've got something I want to say.'

Roulla quickly retorted, 'You've always got something to say!'

He laughed. 'No, listen, it's serious.' He looked around the room. 'I mean this, everybody, I love you all so much. You've become, well, don't misunderstand, closer than family to me. And, well, Nick is kinda special. I mean...' He laughed. 'Well, and now his sister is like another sister and friend to me.'

Chrissy smiled and blew him a kiss. 'Well, it's you two that I have some news for. When I was with Chrissy some weeks ago, as I looked at her, it was strange. Like I recognised something in her. Anyway, I asked Rick to help me do some research.'

Slowly and dramatically, he pulled out the piece of paper. 'Rick got this from Catherine House. You know, the archives of birth registrations. Anyway, to cut a long story short, your mum's maiden name was Richmond. Her mother's maiden name was Townsend and—hang on tight to this one—her mother's name was Goldstein, whose mother's name was Katz, whose mother's name was Shevitz. In other words, Nick and Chrissy are so Jewish that if they were in Nazi Germany, they would have been selected to die. Also, if they wanted to immigrate to Israel, they could become Israeli citizens. It's all to do with having Jewish blood within four generations on your mother's side. The reason for your hair and complexion, Chrissy, has nothing to do with the milkman. It's called genetic generation skip. You're Jewish, babe, and so are you, Nick.'

Chrissy put both hands over her mouth and, squealing with delight, began bobbing up and down on the spot. Roulla's eyes widened as she looked at Nick, who got up and walked over to the window. Deeply moved with emotion, he turned around, and walked towards Kenny. Looking at his dear friend, he then threw his arms around him and began to weep.

The atmosphere erupted into a lively discussion at all the implications. After a few moments, Chrissy walked over to Kenny. 'There is something in the kitchen I want to show you.'

Kenny hobbled on his cane behind her. On the counter was a gift wrapped in shiny green paper, which she shyly held out to Kenny. Leaning against the counter, he

122

slowly unwrapped the paper, finding himself holding a small Rupert Bear. He looked at Chrissy, a smile slowly splitting his face from ear to ear. Then, throwing his head back, he began to laugh as though he had been set free from a nightmare. 'You've given me my Rupert back! He's exactly like the one I lost. Oh, Chrissy, I love you,' he said as he took her into his arms.

29

Roulla walked up and down in the front room. Her mother and father were seated on the couch in their usual position. 'You realise that all this suspense is probably going to damage my chances of leading a healthy balanced remainder to my life. I mean, the Chinese water treatment is one thing, but this is almost Machiavellian.'

Mr Kyriacou interrupted. 'Machae who?'

Roulla replied, 'Machiavelli. You know, he ran a Greek restaurant in Nicosea and he got nicked for serving cat food in his mousaka.'

Mr Kyriacou looked confused. 'I never heard of him. Have you?' he asked his wife.

'No, I'm kidding, Dad. Sorry. Honest, though, please tell me what's going on. I can barely stand it.'

Roulla's father smiled. 'We think Nick is a fine boy and we are happy for you both to be married.'

Roulla gasped. 'Are you serious? You mean we really can? You are going to give us your blessing?' Roulla started to cry and threw her arms around them both. 'Oh, Mummy, Daddy, I'm so happy. I love you so much. Thank you.'

30

Nick was lying face down on his sleeping bag reading his Bible. 'Hey, listen to this one, man. "Anyone who looks at a woman lustfully has already committed adultery with her in his heart." That is thermonuclear heavy, man! Heavy!'

Huss looked over from the table where he was writing. He kept a regular diary and would go back over the events of the month and monitor his emotions and his spiritual life. Now he echoed Nick, 'Heavy!'

The telephone rang and Huss answered. 'Kenny, man, how you doing?'

Kenny replied, 'Are you guys in tonight? If so, I'm coming over in a minicab.'

Huss replied, 'Welcome, your kinsman is here as well. Right now he's meditating on some of the more complicated aspects of our faith.'

Kenny hung up and Huss went back to his diary. After fifteen minutes the front doorbell rang and Kenny hobbled in. Sitting down, he sighed, 'O.K. I'm going to get straight to the point.

'Since meeting you guys, I found myself becoming interested in Jesus. However, as I've studied, I've learned that down through history, the Christians have persecuted the Jews. If Christians are supposed to be like Jesus, then I am confused.'

Huss nodded in agreement. 'You're right to be confused. To be honest, the actions of such people also confuses us. But, I think that it is dangerous to dismiss what God has to say about himself, just because of the perversions of man. Only Jesus truly reveals the heart of God, and the only sensible thing is to look at the life of Jesus.'

'O.K. then, Huss, give it to me in one line. What is it you believe in actual concrete terms?'

Huss pondered for a moment and then spoke. 'I think it would have to be, that sinful men and women can only be made right before a holy God by the blood of Jesus, which was shed to wash away our sin.'

Kenny sighed again. 'I thought it was going to be something like that. I mean, believing and loving is one thing. But that belief is not, well, if you want it, take it if it suits you. If not, don't worry because everything will be O.K.' Frowning, he asked, 'Lay it on me straight. What happens if you don't believe in Jesus?'

Huss had a deeply compassionate look in his eyes. 'The Bible says that you are then separated from God for ever.'

Kenny looked across at Nick and then back to Huss. 'All right, all right. Now we're really getting down to business. What have I got to do to avoid that?'

Huss smiled. 'Nothing.'

Kenny snapped back, 'It sounds like a shaft. Are you saying that I'm not good enough? What do you mean, nothing?'

Huss looked deep into Kenny's eyes. 'Kenny, Jesus did it all. It's not a matter of being good enough, or of doing something to earn God's love. You remember how every year the priest went into the holy place to kill a lamb to pay for Israel's sins? Well, Jesus is our atonement. When he went to the Cross, he went as the perfect Lamb of God, taking our sins upon himself. The special thing about him is that he arose from the dead. That means we don't need any more sacrifices to pay for sin. His blood is enough.

'When I see that Jesus died for me, personally, and that there is nothing I can do to make myself right with God, then I can pray, "God have mercy on me a sinner." ' Huss paused and then continued to speak. 'At that point, when God looks at me, he doesn't see my heart full of sin, but he sees the blood of Jesus. Kenny, God loves you. That is why Jesus died in your place.'

Kenny stood up. 'Thanks, that made things a little clearer for me. Can I use your telephone?'

Huss nodded, and Kenny dialled Chrissy. 'Chris, it's me. Can I come over now? We've got to talk.'

He hung up and dialled again. 'Yeah, listen, I need a minicab. I'm in Stoke Newington.'

Kenny and Chrissy walked slowly down along the south bank of the Thames between Waterloo and Westminster Bridge. Kenny hobbled slightly with his cane, but it was evident that the healing process of his young body had won the battle against the armies of prejudice and hate. It was a cool day, although the sun hung high in the blue sky. Kenny stopped, leaned against the wall, and looked over into the river. Chrissy was wearing a pair of white dungarees and a grass-green blouse. Her raven-black hair hung neatly over her shoulders, with the occasional fugitive tassel breaking away from her head and dancing to the command of the gentle wind that breathed from the direction of the river.

Kenny had shaken her when he had come around the other evening to talk about Jesus. He had been able to sweep her into the intensity of the situation. Now, however, he seemed more at peace. 'You know, Chrissy, I think every argument that I could ever have conjured up about not being a believer has been removed. There's no resistance left in that way. Yet, now something else is stopping me. I can't explain.'

A pigeon landed just a few feet away from Kenny and Chrissy. Instinctively, they both stood still, not wanting to frighten him. Their visitor walked along the wall towards them, then, cocking his head to look at them, flew off.

Kenny spoke. 'You know when I came around the other night to talk to you? Well, when I was sitting in the minicab, I thought to myself, tonight I will become a believer in Jesus. But then, even though I felt that I can be a believer with a clear Jewish conscience, I'm not sure that I want to.'

Chrissy nodded. 'I have similar struggles, but I think my biggest one is that I want whatever we do, to do it together. Part of me seems to say that's not right because it is an individual and personal decision. Yet, I can't explain how much a part of you that I feel. Love really is painful as well as beautiful, isn't it?'

Kenny looked at Chrissy, then reached into his pocket and pulled out his little Rupert Bear. Smiling, he spoke. 'This was so unexpected, it was unbelievable. I thought I had laid down all the barriers between us, but then when you gave Rupert to me it was as if you opened up this great never-ending chamber in my soul and then filled it with your love. Somehow you really have set me free.' He paused. 'But it's interesting, I have another chamber that I know only God can fill.'

Chrissy smiled. 'Why don't we both become believers, you know, right here? Pray to Jesus and all that?'

Kenny laughed nervously. 'I can't, babe; I can't explain it but I just can't seem to do it.'

31

Huss and Angie had gone with Sheila and Rick for a walk through Clissold Park. Sheila and Rick had walked on ahead, and now the sun was beginning to set, the sky seeming to burst with an interweaving of pastel colours. Huss turned and smiled at Angie, then spoke. 'You know, Angie, it is just so exciting to see the way God is working in your life. I think what makes my heart sing, is that you have actually forgiven me.'

'It wasn't me, it was Jesus in me, who taught me to forgive.'

'Angie, I love you. Will you marry me?'

Angie started backward, shock on her face. 'Wait a minute. Just because I have forgiven you, don't think that we can just pick up where we were.' Frowning, she spoke emphatically, 'Don't push me!'

'I'm sorry. I tend to forget that you're not at the same spot as me. It's hard to think that you don't feel the same.'

Angie's eyes filled with tears, and her heart tightened with fear. 'You have no right to expect anything from me. After all, it was you who wounded me, then deserted me. Now get out of my space.'

Turning, she ran away from him, tears blinding her eyes.

That night, the phone rang for Angie. 'Hello? This is Huss.'

A seemingly unreasonable fear gripped Angie, and she snapped, 'I don't have anything to say to you!'

'Wait! Please don't hang up. I wanted to tell you I was sorry. You are right. I guess I am still the selfish person you used to know. It's like because I'm the man, I have the right to have my needs met, whenever I want them. That is very wrong of me, and I wanted to tell you I'm sorry for pushing you. I will give you all the space you want, only please give me a chance to prove to you that I really love you?'

'Hmm. Only time will tell if that is true,' Angie responded non-committally.

32

Viewing her reaction to Huss, Angie realised she was indeed more emotionally fragile than they both had realised. She felt an almost childlike dependency on the group, and especially on Sheila, who had become like a mother to her. Now as Angie walked down the main street in Tottenham, she felt a sense of accomplishment. It had been a real victory, going into the shop and actually making a choice. Nestled in her black and yellow plastic bag was an oil painting set and a book on how to start painting as a hobby.

As she walked, she noticed the trees. They were green, yet had an almost fatigued sadness about them. It was as if they were using all their energy to draw enough oxygen from the polluted atmosphere just to survive. The sensitivity of the moment seemed to penetrate the emotional structure of her inner self.

Suddenly, and unexpectedly, a little Pakistani girl, with long pigtails and wearing a pink Asian style top and trousers, came running around the corner and bumped right into her, nearly knocking her over. Following close behind were two young English boys, about ten or eleven years old. As she bumped into Angie, she instinctively clutched her around the waist, holding tightly and crying in fear, 'They're going to get me!'

The two boys stopped in their tracks and stared.

Then, sneering, the older one snarled, 'We'll get you later!' In a moment, they were gone.

Angie hugged the fragile little girl who was now sobbing uncontrollably. Resting her plastic bag against the wall, she took out her handkerchief to wipe the little girl's eyes. 'What's your name?' she whispered.

Large brown, tear-filled eyes looked trustingly up at Angie. 'Yamina.'

'Where do you live, Yamina?' Angie asked as she wiped another tear away.

The child explained where she lived. Angie took her little hand, as they walked toward her block of flats. 'Why were those boys chasing you, Yamina?'

'Because I'm a Pakistani.'

Angie sighed as she squeezed the little girl's hand and thought of how the wickedness of prejudice could invade such young lives. Together they walked up the stairway to Yamina's flat. There was rotting rubbish lying in the corner and the stench of urine combined to fill the air with a stale, almost pungent smell, causing a wave of nausea to sweep over her. Then Angie noticed a tree in the courtyard, which had that same tired look as the trees on the High Street. She turned and looked at Yamina and realised that this little child, instead of being full of life and childlike joy, also had the same fatigued look about her, as if she, too, was using all her strength just to survive.

Yamina rapped on the letter-box and almost instantly the door opened. A Pakistani woman in her mid-thirties opened the door. She, too, was wearing the same silky-style Pakistani top and trousers. She wore dangling gold earrings and numerous gold wrist bangles. She looked as if, when she was younger, she had been a strikingly beautiful woman. Now old before her time, she was overweight, and had a somewhat harassed look about her. She spoke in another language to Yamina, who replied in the same. Then turning, the woman smiled at Angie and ushered her into the small, yet tidy flat.

A strong smell of curry hung in the air. Angie thought it almost seemed to come from the wallpaper. Yamina asked her to sit down, as the woman went into the kitchen to prepare tea. Angie looked around the room. A large green carpet with a picture of a mosque hung on one wall. Near it was a large brass mirror, filled with photographs of varying sizes, which were tucked into the corners in the small crevices around the mirror's frame.

'Does your mummy speak any English, Yamina?'

Yamina shook her head, 'She's not my mummy, she's my auntie. I've never had a mother or father. They were killed in a train crash when I was a baby.'

Angie looked at this precious child and thought her heart would break. It always seemed that some people had the good things in life happen to them, while others had all the bad. Soon Yamina's aunt returned and laid a small tray down on the coffee table. There was one cup of milky tea and a plate of biscuits next to it. The aunt spoke roughly to Yamina, who replied timidly. As the child handed Angie the tea, Angie asked, 'What did she say to you?'

Yamina looked at her aunt and then back at Angie. 'Oh, nothing really.' Her aunt spoke again, and Angie's heart seemed, by intuition, to put all the pieces together. Caring for Yamina was a burden, a responsibility, an unwanted duty to perform.

Angie felt a surge of tenderness rise in her heart. 'Yamina, ask your auntie if you could come and visit me and my friends some day.'

Yamina translated. At first, the older woman was cautious. She looked at Angie, almost studying her face. Finally she spoke and Yamina excitedly said it would be all right.

For the next half an hour, Angie asked Yamina questions about herself and her life. The child had no toys and no friends. As Angie walked to the door to leave, Yamina instinctively placed her little hand in hers. Angie opened the door and turned towards her, bent down, and gave her a hug. The little girl clutched her around the neck, whispering in her ear, 'I wish you were my mummy.'

It was as if a spear pierced deep into Angie's soul. She touched the child's cheek, and whispered back, 'I can't be your mummy, but I would like to be your special friend.' Then kissing her on the forehead, she left. Yamina hung over the balcony waving to Angie as she walked away from the flats. As she walked, she experienced a mixture of pain and of joy. Something profound had just happened. She who desperately needed to be loved by others, had now found someone who desperately needed her, and in giving of herself, she had found fulfilment. The feeling was so profound that Angie began to weep. Through her tears, she began to praise God. 'O Lord, I can't explain what it feels like to be needed. It is so wonderful. Thank you so much for letting me be in the right place when this dear child needed me. Lord, how wonderful it would be, if you could use me to love hurting children like Yamina. Thank you, Lord, for your love. Please protect little Yamina.'

33

Nick ran from the taxi into the front entrance of the hospital. He turned sharply down the corridor and began to look around. His heart pounded violently, as a terrifying panic swept over him. Surely it must be a mistake, for he had only spoken to Roulla on the telephone the night before. At the end of the corridor he could see Roulla's mother and father talking to a nurse. Nick slowed his pace, fear overwhelmed him and he closed his eyes. Opening them, it seemed as if they were a blur, as if they were at the end of a long tunnel that he was sliding down, unable to control the movements of his arms and legs. Finally he stood beside them. Unaware that tears were falling down his face, he spoke in a whisper. 'How is she? Can I see her?'

Roulla's mother, who was sobbing brokenly, was being comforted by a nurse. Her father, pale with agony, spoke hesitantly. 'She has a brain haemorrhage.' A sob tore his frame, then he continued. 'It was just out of the blue. She's never been ill in her life, yet they say it's a brain haemorrhage.' Mr Kyriacou shook his head in confusion. 'It all happened so suddenly. This morning when she came down to breakfast, she complained of a headache. But you know how she is, and she just joked about it. But then a few minutes later as she was eating some Weetabix, she moaned, clutched her head, then fell to the floor unconscious. When the ambulance came, they put an oxygen mask on her, then carried her to the ambulance, but she was so pale, it was like she was dead.'

The words were like a sledge-hammer being smashed into Nick's face, causing him to feel as if he would vomit. 'No! It can't be!' At that moment, he wanted to smash something up, furniture, property, his father, the doctors, anything or anybody.

'You can't see her now. She's in the intensive care unit. They're going to try to move her down to the Maudesly Hospital near King's College down by Camberwell.'

Nick's mind began to close down. 'South of the river? Why south of the river?'

'Because Maudesly is the only hospital that handles these kind of cases,' Roulla's father answered, then his voice began to quiver. 'Nick, they said to me, "Mr Kyriacou, your little girl may die." ' At this, the older man began to sob helplessly.

Nick cried out in the depths of his soul, 'Lord, help me, help us.' Reaching out, he put his arms around Roulla's mother and father, and together they wept as he held them. Then, sniffing and taking a deep breath, he began to speak. 'I wanted to call you both mother and father since the first time we met.' He paused. 'Mother and Father, let me pray with you.' There in the hospital corridor, Nick led Androulla's parents before God's throne. He pleaded that Roulla would not be taken from them, and then asked God to give them strength to face what lay ahead. A peace seemed to descend upon the little group, as they stood together.

34

Roulla lay motionless on the stretcher that had just been put into the ambulance. Although her eyes were closed she was aware of what was happening. The medication seemed to be helping, as the vomiting had now ceased. Every so often she felt as if she were drifting and then other times she felt as if she were falling. The ambulance started its journey and its movement seemed to exaggerate the feelings of drifting and falling. Something seemed to say that now was the time to die, but an inner peace in her soul reigned over any fear of the unknown.

Meanwhile at Huss's flat, Huss gripped Nick, almost in a bear-hug. Then Nick began to pace up and down the room, tears streaming down his cheeks as he shouted at the same time. 'I can't handle it, man! It's the ultimate wind-up, the last straw! Where is God in all of this? Roulla's a nice girl, she never hurt anybody. Why does God let stuff like this happen? I thought he was a God of love. Well, where is his love in all of this?

Huss sighed. 'I'm afraid there are no easy answers to life, Nick.'

Just then the doorbell rang. Huss opened it to find Rick, Sheila and Angie standing on the doorstep.

Sheila spoke softly. 'We wanted to be with you, Nick, because we love Roulla too. The doctors should be operating on her soon. We thought we'd come around and pray for them, that God would help them to save Roulla's life.'

Nick rubbed his eyes with the back of his sleeve, trying to hold back the tears. Angie walked over to him and placed her hand on his shoulder. 'It's O.K. to cry. We've all been crying too. It's such a horrible shock.'

Nick began to weep again. 'It's so unfair! What did Roulla do to deserve this?'

'You're right. It is unfair!' Sheila frowned and shook her head. 'It's not because Roulla did something wrong. God wasn't trying to punish her. He isn't like that. But he does promise to take every bad thing that happens to his children and turn it into something beautiful. I think our part is to trust him, even when we don't understand what he is doing, or why. Right now, we just need to cling to him.'

'Maybe God will use this time to touch others,' added Angie, her eyes moist with tears. 'I know that it hurts so much. But sometimes God uses our pain to get our attention. Maybe we need to talk to him about it.'

The group knelt on the floor, and at first all that was heard were gentle sobs. Then Nick began to pray. 'Lord, I've been so selfish. All I've been thinking about is my pain, and what I will do if Roulla dies. O Lord, forgive me. I love her so much, I just don't know what I would do if she dies. O Lord, please spare her. If she is there in hospital because of me, please forgive me. Lord, she is yours, and you love her. If your plan is to take her to heaven, please give me the strength to accept that. Whatever is best for Roulla, is what we want.' At that point, Nick began to weep brokenly.

In spite of the tears, a peace settled on the room as each person wept and prayed for God to heal Roulla if it was his will. God's Spirit seemed to touch their hearts with a new depth of compassion as they began to pray for Roulla's parents, and for all who would come in contact with Roulla during her illness.

Meanwhile Roulla was wheeled into the hospital, with thoughts of Nick and her parents playing on the screen of her mind. During the operation, she began to walk along the narrow corridor in her soul. At the end was a door, which was slowly opening. A great wafting light of purity and undefiled glory seemed to be pouring through. She was there, now the time had come to gasp her last breath, to bid her loved ones farewell in her heart and then to collapse into the arms of Jesus. She stood before the door basking in the light of eternal rest and then slowly she began to drift. As she fell upwards and away from the door, the pain began to return to her body. After some time, she became aware of sounds around her. Her lips moved. 'Nickos, dear Nickos, I can hear you calling me.'

Back in Huss's flat, the group continued praying, trusting God to do something special. The peacefulness was shattered by the shrill ringing of the telephone. Everyone turned pale, as Huss rose from his knees. Answering the phone, he quickly turned to Nick. 'It's for you.'

Hesitantly Nick got to his feet and walked slowly to the phone. With trembling hands, he took the receiver and held it to his ear. 'Nick, this is Roulla's father. Good news!' He laughed for joy. 'They've done an emergency operation and thank God she is going to be all right! Nick? Nick? Are you there? What's happening...?'

The receiver had dropped from Nick's hand, as he walked in a daze, saying over and over with wonder in his voice, 'God heard! God heard!', then collapsed onto the bed in relief.

Huss picked up the telephone receiver. 'Yeah, hi, Mr Kriaa...' He couldn't pronounce the name. 'Nick's O.K., he's just overcome with relief. I'll get him to ring you back when he can get himself together.'

After Nick re-entered the world of rationality, the group of friends sat down and began to pray. Nick joyfully prayed, 'O Lord, thank you for today. Angie was right, Lord. I knew I loved Androulla, but almost losing her has shown me how precious she is. It's like, Lord, you are telling me to value her, like a beautiful diamond. I feel like I want to be gentle towards her and to give her care for everything in her life. Thank you, Lord, thank you.'

Angie whispered a prayer, 'I love Roulla so much, Jesus. Thank you for bringing her back to us.'

The earlier atmosphere of mourning was replaced by joy. Each was intensely aware that Jesus was there with them, sharing in their joy, even as he had shared their tears. Life had suddenly become very beautiful and very precious, and each of the five in the room sensed a bond between them as they had walked through the valley of the shadow of death together.

Huss continued, 'Jesus, you're terrific. Thank you for what you're doing in all of our lives. Somehow make us a source of healing to hurting people in this wounded city in which we live.'

35

Nick stepped down from the train and onto the platform at Denmark Hill. It wasn't that far south of the river but he still felt uncomfortable. There was something so familiar about north-east London that his security was somewhat wrapped up in its geography. He stood on the platform, which was about fifty feet below the street level, just to ponder for a moment. The tall walls just beside the track for some reason made him think about mountaineering, which set him thinking of all those nutters who spend indescribable amounts of money and time risking their lives just to climb a mountain. They didn't do anything when they got there but would just hang around for twenty more minutes, talk to each other about how good it was to be there and then leave.

A noise coming from up the stairs filtered through into his thoughts, shaking him back from the irrationality of mountain climbing to the present time and place. Shouting was going on above him and, curiously, he walked up the stairs in the direction of the noise. A young Irish girl, wearing a faded T-shirt that said 'Support Your Local Poet', was standing in the ticket hall. A West Indian railway worker was shouting at her.

'Look, the ticket counter is closed, I tell you. Besides, I'm too tired to open it for you. You will just have to pay at the other end.'

The Irish supporter of local poets was shouting back, 'I don't want the hassle of paying at the other end. You give me a ticket here!'

Nick spoke to them both. 'Calm down, you're winding each other up; you'll do your blood pressure in.'

The Irish girl immediately turned on Nick. 'Listen, brick-face, take your advice somewhere else.'

The railway man chipped in, 'Mind your own business, man.'

Nick looked at them both, threw his hands in the air and walked out into the street. 'South of the river,' he thought to himself, 'they're all nutters! And I bet they go mountaineering at the week-ends.'

After walking the short distance from the station to the hospital, Nick was soon by Roulla's bed. She lay completely flat and perfectly still, her eyes were closed but occasionally her eyelids would give a gentle flutter. Her head had been completely shaved but her baldness was covered in part by a tightly-bound bandage that covered the top of her head and came down around the side of her face under her chin. There were wires coming from the inside of the bandages that were attached to a machine, the monitor of which had white lines dancing across the screen. An intravenous drip was in her left arm.

Nick sat beside her bed and reached out gently and held her hand. Seeing her lying so helpless, sent great waves of warmth rushing through his body and soul. After a short while, as if aware of his presence, Roulla opened her eyes. When she focused on Nick, her eyes lit up and she smiled.

Nick leaned forward and spoke to her. 'I love you, Roulla.'

Roulla tried to speak but only garbled sounds came out of her mouth. As the realisation hit Nick that this articulate powerful personality was unable to speak normally, he felt anger rising within him.

Roulla closed her eyes and immediately drifted back to sleep. Nick looked at her olive pure and creamy skin. Her night-dress had small Disney animals embroidered along the top around her neck. The reality of her innocence, along with the pragmatic knowledge that she might be a vegetable, penetrated Nick's mind.

He stood up abruptly, knocking over his chair. Brusquely, he grabbed a nurse. 'I want to see her doctor. Now!'

The nurse calmly picked up the chair and then led Nick away from the bed. 'She actually has three doctors, but let's see if we can get somebody to see you.'

Within a few minutes, Nick found himself shaking hands with a young woman doctor, dressed casually in blue jeans and a white medical coat. Nick spoke. 'What's happened to her? Why can't she speak? It's as if she is completely messed up.'

The doctor demonstrated a completely professional air, yet combined it with genuine compassion. 'You're her fiancé, yes?... Good. Well, let me explain. What has happened to Androulla is that one of the arteries in her head had swollen and began to leak blood into her brain. This is what we call a congenital condition, which means that there was a weakness there from the time of birth. What we had to do was to operate and just clip that difficult area. Unfortunately, the area we had to work in is quite delicate. It's the part of the brain that both receives and produces speech.'

Nick was in awe that this doctor had communicated something as complicated as brain surgery in such simple terms. 'What you're saying, Doc, is that she can't understand me when I speak and she can't speak to me in return.'

The doctor nodded. 'Absolutely, but...'

Nick interrupted, 'But that means she'll be a vegetable for the rest of her life.'

The doctor smiled with gentle patience. 'No, it's not

143

quite like that. We hope it's only temporary. Normally, it should only last a few hours but she's been like this for a day. I'm afraid we really have to just sit and wait.'

To Nick, the very idea of sitting and waiting had no appeal. 'But she recognises me.'

The doctor continued to smile patiently. 'Absolutely. She will be completely normal in every way except in understanding speech and then being able to speak in return.'

Nick, greatly subdued, returned to Roulla's bed. He held her hand, then kissed each of her fingers. In his heart he prayed, 'Lord Jesus, I'm in for good with this precious girl. I don't care what it takes. I'm going to love her and care for her for the rest of her life.' As he prayed, he thought, 'Loving a girl as a believer has awesome responsibilities.'

Several days had passed, and Roulla was still unable to speak. Early in the morning, the phone rang and Nick answered it.

Angie was on the other end. 'Nick, I've had an idea about Roulla. I was praying for you both yesterday when it hit me. Anyway, I went to the library and got this book about sign language for deaf people. What you could do is teach Roulla some simple signs like cup, spoon, and stuff. Well, if it works, you could have a whole language together.'

Nick felt electricity pass through his brain. 'Angie, that's brilliant.'

Angie continued, 'Well, I didn't want you to get stitched up about it if it didn't work, so I rang the hospital and they say they don't mind if you have a try.'

When they hung up, Nick turned to Huss. 'You know, Huss, you would have to be a loghead not to believe in Jesus after what is happening in all our lives. I just can't believe what is going on with Angie; it's like she's come of age or something.'

36

Chrissy and Sheila sat in the kitchen drinking coffee. Sheila wore a bright red shirt and black trousers. Chrissy had her long hair pulled back in a pony tail and was wearing a white T-shirt with white running shorts. She was into jogging now, and had just returned from running.

Sheila smiled. 'You know, you're really beautiful. I used to be really jealous of you when I first saw you.'

Chrissy looked uncomfortable. 'Don't say that, Sheila. It winds me up.'

Sheila looked up seriously, 'But I'm being honest. I talked to Rick; he's very good about this kind of stuff. He said you were an absolute turn-on but that he only saw you as someone who needed to be loved for who you are.'

Chrissy smiled. 'Rick said that? Straight up? It's awesome, really, about your group. It's like everyone cares about each other. I know Roulla and my brother are going to get married and that, but it's like, she's my sister. I can't bear to think of her being messed up.'

Sheila looked lovingly at her friend. 'Listen, I'm not trying to get into your box or anything, but what's stopping you from becoming a believer?'

Chrissy fidgeted with her spoon, then stood up. 'It's hard, really, because I want to but I am desperate about

Kenny. It's like if I go it alone, it's one more time that he's been left out and left alone.'

Sheila looked concerned. 'Is that all that bothers you?'

Chrissy sat back down. 'No. I guess I never pictured myself messing around, you know, living with a guy. Then when I did, I felt so guilty. I guess I really hated myself most when I met Kenny, and wished that I was pure. But it's too late for me.' Chrissy began to weep and Sheila reached over and put her arms around her.

'Oh, Chrissy, I'm sorry that you're hurting. But it isn't too late. God loves to make us pure again.'

Chrissy spoke through her tears. 'I feel so wretched. I don't think God could ever accept me because I knew what I was doing was wrong.'

Sheila reached on top of the fridge, and brought down her Bible. 'Listen to this.' Sheila thumbed through the pages to Isaiah. 'I, even I, am he who blots out your transgressions, for my own sake, and remembers your sins no more.'

Chrissy looked confused. 'I don't understand it. I'm sorry.'

Sheila put her Bible down on the table. 'You know that we can't earn God's forgiveness on our own. But God doesn't forgive us because it's like a duty. He wants to forgive us! It gives him pleasure to forgive us. Then once he removes a sin, it is gone for ever.'

Chrissy frowned, her eyes filled with tears. 'I can't hold back any longer.' Bowing her head, she began to pray, 'Jesus. I need you. I've done so many wrong things. Please forgive me, and take it all away, so that I can be clean again, like Sheila says. Oh Jesus.'

Sheila reached out, hugging Chrissy as tears of joy spilled down both their cheeks. In the quiet of the kitchen, a peacefulness enfolded them, while in heaven, angels were rejoicing.

37

Nick picked up the sign language book from Angie and then made his way from Highbury Corner over to Victoria on the Underground. He eagerly began to study the book on the train, practising the signs with his hands. An Indian man who sat opposite him, tried not to look at Nick but found himself spellbound. Nick, however, was oblivious to everything around him, as he made his way across London.

Roulla stirred as Nick sat down beside her. He purposely chose not to speak. Angie had suggested that he communicate with her as if she were deaf as well as unable to speak. Kissing his finger, he touched her lips. He then held his heart, smiled and pointed at her. Her eyes sparkled, then slowly she brought her hand up and kissed her finger and touched his lips. Nick jumped up in excitement, feeling like dancing for joy. Thinking better of it, he propped open his book on the bedside table. Picking up a glass he showed it to her, then carefully signed out the letters. She looked at him confused. He repeated this several times with no response.

He had tucked a hard-boiled egg in his pocket, which he now pulled out, signing the letters for egg. There was still no response. So he decided to let her rest, holding her hand and gazing deeply into her brown eyes. She smiled and kissed her finger and then placed it on his lips again. He did the same. Suddenly he realised what was happening. They were communicating that they loved each other. He pointed towards heaven, kissed his finger, then pointed upwards again. Roulla smiled in understanding, and duplicated the sign. The effect was magnetic. Nick kissed her hand, laughing with joy. He picked up the egg again, pointed to it, then signed out the letters. Roulla smiled, then signed out the letters in response. Nick suddenly felt that this was the emotional high point of his life. The tender strand of communication between them had been cut by tragedy. Now a river of love flowed from one to the other. Roulla's eyes were alive with life and joy. Her old self began to sparkle through this experience. Nick kissed his finger and touched her lips. Truly, he loved her more than he loved his own life, he thought to himself.

38

Kenny lay flat on his back in his bed and looked at the ceiling. To his left was his dressing table. Above the mirror was a photograph of Chrissy. She was so beautiful, he thought to himself. Sitting by the mirror was his Rupert Bear, who was now associated with Chrissy. How he loved her, he thought.

Now he lay in turmoil of spirit for Chrissy had told him that evening that she had become a believer. It was unreal, yet the fact of its reality would not let him go. The agony of the situation was like a terminal illness. It was like he could not escape it. He tried to move his mind onto something else, but could not. It was complete and total obsession. The hard pragmatic side of him surfaced. He would not marry her. He had seen the way that things went with these people who became believers. They changed. Oh, it was slow, but they always changed. Gradually, they began to spend all their time reading their Bibles. It was fine enough from their point of view but a marriage where one is and one is not just wasn't on. The very thoughts were like a surgical knife, but unfortunately, in this surgery, there was no anaesthetic.

He knew that she would be thinking the same kind of thoughts. Her whole idea would be how to get Kenny to become a believer. Something inside said no. He couldn't identify what it was; there was a certain sense of inner fatigue that seemed to be gnawing away at his will. The fading light filtering through the curtains revealed that night was coming. Night—the very word had a ring of finality to it, creating a sense of despair. He remembered Eli Wiesal's book, *Night*, about his life in Auschwitz as a young child, and the horrors of the never-ending night that suffocated the breath of millions and the hope of a planet. A part of him wanted to die. He knew that it was impossible to fake becoming a believer. It had to be either the real thing or not at all. Sitting up, he realised that he had to talk to Chrissy again.

The telephone rang in Rick and Sheila's flat and Chrissy answered it.

'Hi, Kenny. Are you feeling any better? I'm sorry that I didn't tell you in person.'

Kenny responded, 'It's O.K. I understand, but we've got to see each other to talk this thing through, because I've got this real premonition that it's not going to work between us. I know. I just know.'

'No,' she responded, stunned, feeling as if her world had caved in. Perhaps the fear of this had been partly what had held her back from making the decision earlier. Trembling, she sat down on the stairs, numb from the shock. Speaking barely in a whisper, she protested, 'Don't say that! Surely it can work out. Can't we just accept each other just like we are? I love you.' She started to cry, 'I need you, I can't live without you.'

Kenny groaned. 'I know, I know. I love you too. It's not easy for me either. But I know what happens. Slowly you will change. Slowly every breath that you breathe will ultimately belong to Jesus. I've seen it in the others.'

Chrissy pleaded, 'Let me see you, just be with you for a few moments. I know that we can make it work.'

Kenny took a deep breath, 'I'm sick, Chrissy. I've got to go away for just a little while and think. I'll ring you again sometime.'

'Promise me you will ring again. Kenny, don't finish it. Please!' The telephone clicked as gently, and with great pain, Kenny hung up the receiver. Chrissy, who was in the house alone, began to sob uncontrollably as though her heart would break.

Kenny walked into his room, took a suitcase from his cupboard and packed some clothes. He paused, looking out the window. A cold shudder ran through his soul, for night had come. He checked his wallet for his Access card, bank card and cheque book; it was time to go sick for a few days and think things through. He took one last look at Rupert Bear, smiled a sad smile, then walked down the stairs into the night.

Heartbroken, Chrissy lay quietly on the couch. The clock had just chimed two and, weary from weeping, she lay looking out the window at the silhouette of the houses. In the distance she heard the sound of a train gently clattering through the city. The sound of trains in the middle of the night had always been comforting to her. Now the sound was a painful reminder of Kenny leaving. Surely he needed her, even as she needed him. How would she be able to cope? They loved each other.

Wasn't being a believer supposed to be wonderful? Doubts began to sow themselves into her heart and mind. Perhaps God was punishing her. Perhaps he loved the world in general but she had done too many bad things to be really accepted by him. Maybe she wasn't even really a believer. Slowly she slipped into a sad and restless sleep.

Nick and Huss were shaken awake by the sound of the telephone ringing. Nick's immediate reaction was that Roulla had had a relapse and was dying. 'Oh Jesus, let her be all right,' he prayed, as he dragged himself out of his sleeping bag and reached for the phone.

'Kenny, man, what's going on? It's half past three in

the morning.' Huss had sat up, looked groggily across the room and then turned over.

Kenny's voice was shaking. 'I don't know what to do, Nick. Have you seen Chrissy?'

'No, man, I was out until late at the hospital.'

'You know she became a believer? Well, I'm all screwed up inside. My head is just about to leave the earth's atmosphere. I never thought she would do it without me.'

'Where are you?'

'Nick, I want you to look after Chrissy for me. I have to get away to do some thinking, and I'm worried about her. Look after her, hear?'

'Kenny...' His voice echoed down an empty line.

Two days later, a letter arrived for Chrissy from Kenny, which said,

> 'Dear Chrissy,
>
> I know it is hard for you to understand, but I need to get away to think. The very foundations of my life are shaking, and I just don't know what to do. I am a Jew, and now you have become a believer. Oh, yes, there is Jewish blood in you, but you have never known or understood your Jewish identity. To me, life is being a Jew. If you had come into the synagogue, there would have been no problem. Even as I say that, I know you are thinking that I don't go regularly myself. What does it matter? I really don't know, and that is what I have to find out.
>
> One way or another, I will be in touch with you. If I can get past the barriers of becoming a believer, then we can be married. I love you, and I am sorry for the pain I am causing you.'

It was signed 'Kenny', but had no forwarding address.

Chrissy held the letter to her, rocking back and forth as she wept. After a few moments, she began to pray, 'O Lord. Please help him to find you. Please, Lord.'

39

Roulla was sitting up in bed. For the past weeks, Nick had been teaching her sign language, and she was able to talk with her hands quite well. As a couple, they had become quite a phenomenon to both the staff and the patients in the hospital. The nurses had often talked about how romantic it all was, kissing fingers and then placing them on the lips. It was all so pure and unselfish, one of them had commented.

Tonight Nick's heart had felt as if it would explode with joy. He had had his eyes on an engagement ring in the window of a jeweller's shop in Harringay for weeks. Not wanting to dip into his savings account, as they would need that to begin married life, he was also determined not to borrow money to buy it. Then he realised that his stereo hi-fi system, which he had bought on the 'Never, Never' a couple of years ago, was worth quite a bit. Last night he had sold it. Even if it was a steal for the bloke who bought it, he told himself, he had the necessary ready. Rushing straight from work to the jewellers, he had purchased the ring.

Once seated on the Piccadilly line from Manor House Station, Nick closed his eyes, imagining Roulla's reaction when she saw the ring. Ahead of him, a young couple with an infant were quarrelling about visiting the husband's mother. 'You always let her manipulate us, and you end up doing what she wants, even if it hurts me,' she complained.

'That's not true. You're just being childish.'

'Please...'

The young man interrupted his wife. 'We won't talk about it any more. In fact, I'm not talking to you again until you realise your duty.'

The two turned away from each other and sat in angry silence. As Nick watched them, he felt sad. Impulsively, he reached forward. 'Here, you two. Do you realise what you are doing? Don't you realise what a precious gift it is to be able to communicate with each other?'

'What's it to you?' The young man sneered, feeling embarrassed that anyone had been listening.

Nick's eyes filled with tears. 'The girl I love nearly died a few weeks ago. She is doing much better but she can't talk. In fact, it seems that I will never hear her voice again. I long for that more than I could tell you. Anyway, we've learned to do sign language together. You see, when you really love someone, you just have to communicate with them. Love finds a way.'

The young couple, moved by Nick's story, looked at each other, and smiled. As the train stopped, and they rose to get off, they turned to Nick. 'Thanks. All the best.'

Roulla's hair was barely growing; the electrodes were gone but a bandage still covered most of her head. She had lost weight but she looked so fresh and pure as she sat slowly signing out words to her beloved. Nick touched her hand, kissed her fingers and placed them on his own lips. She smiled and then they gazed into each other's eyes. 'Close your eyes; I have a surprise for you,' he signed. She smiled and closed her eyes. Reaching into his pocket he took out a little blue box. Then, tenderly, he placed the box in her hand. Her eyes fluttered open and widened in surprise and confusion. Gently he took the box and opened it, revealing a gold ring with a small diamond, nestled in the blue velvet. Roulla looked at the ring and then into Nick's eyes, pointing first to the ring and then to herself. He nodded, then kissing her left hand, he took the ring and gently placed it on her finger. 'I love you, Roulla. Will you marry me?'

Roulla gently wept as she looked at this precious young man who had chosen her to become the object of his love. Through her tears she nodded yes. Then, signing, she said, 'I love you.'

He reached over and kissed her forehead, then signed, 'I thank God for you, my precious flower.' Two nurses stood in the corner and wiped tears from their eyes. It seemed like only moments before the bell rang announcing the end of visiting hours. When Nick was gone, Roulla gazed at the sparkling stone that seemed to send light prancing into all directions like little sparklets dancing on the rocks of the bottom of a waterfall. Warm love poured through her body and mind. She closed her eyes, totally at peace with God and the world.

From the Authors

Dear Friend,

Many people feel wounded, lost, unloved, and totally beyond God's love. Yet all of us, no matter how wounded we are, long to be loved and appreciated.

Perhaps, as you've read this book, you have identified with some situation or character. We would like to say to you that God sees your fears, your guilt, and your pain, and he cares. There is no situation in life that is beyond God's healing power. He loves you no matter how wounded you are.

We, too, care about you. Do write to us, if you need a friend. We would love to hear from you, for we believe you are special.

God bless you,

Bob and Barbara Hitching
5853 Main Street
Elkridge
MD 21227
USA

The Wounded: Part 2

by Bob and Barbara Hitching

If you have enjoyed reading this book, you can find out more about this gang of young people in *The Wounded: Part 2*—another unfolding drama of life in the East End of London.

Agonise with HUSS as he struggles with a heart-rending choice.

Weep with ANGIE as the wounds of the past continue to torture her.

Laugh with NICK and ROULLA as they chart the course of true love.

Follow too the paths of RICK and SHEILA, KENNY and CHRISSY as this unusual group of friends grapple with the pressures of life in the inner city.

 *OM Publishing*